HUMAN HORIZONS SERIES

CHILDREN BEHAVING BADLY

Could My Child Have a Disorder?

ALAN TRAIN

A Condor Book
Souvenir Press (E&A Ltd)

To my wife Vivienne and our four children
Jonathan, Peter, Helen and Matthew

Vincit Qui Patitur: S.T.D.

First published 2000 by
Souvenir Press (Educational & Academic) Ltd,
43 Great Russell Street, London WC1B 3PA

ISBN 0 285 63521 2

Typeset by Rowland Phototypesetting Ltd,
Bury St Edmunds, Suffolk

Printed in Great Britain by
The Guernsey Press Co. Ltd, Guernsey, Channel Islands

Contents

Part One

COMMON CONCERNS

1 Is There Something Wrong with My Child?

Before your child was born you may have been asked whether you wanted a boy or a girl. You probably said that you didn't mind either way, so long as he or she was fit and healthy.

This would be the hope of most parents, not only before their child was born but as he grew older. But in addition to wanting their child to be physically well, parents want him to be happy, to relate well to others and to be just like—and preferably better than!—others in his age group. They want him to do well at school, to have lots of friends and to be successful. In essence they want him to bring them happiness.

Regrettably, as we all know, this cannot be guaranteed. Even if your child has been born without any physical or mental disability it is possible that things could go wrong, that he could change either gradually or suddenly from being a pleasurable responsibility into an unbearable burden. Many parents can vouch for this: it is estimated that two million children in the UK have significant mental health problems that affect their behaviour and the lives of those who care for them. You may have chosen to read this book because you are becoming seriously concerned that all is not well with your child. You may have reached the point where you are beginning to look to the future only with apprehension, even despair.

At one time, you may have been able to laugh about your child's behaviour—you may even have taken a special pride in his 'naughtiness', or found comfort in the way in which his exceptional personality permeated the lives of you and your friends. But the pleasure he once gave you may now be turning into anxiety. Your hopes and aspirations may be changing into doubts and concerns.

In the early days you may have assumed that as your child

became older he would learn to adjust, that his behaviour would change and he would ultimately respond in appropriate ways. Perhaps it became clear that things might not progress so smoothly when he first began to mix with other children. On the other hand, he may have always related well to others—indeed, he may have been very popular—but then you observed a sudden change in him.

Despite everything you have done to help the situation, nothing appears to work. He is a continual source of anxiety—and you do not know what to do about it.

This book has been written to help those parents who can no longer laugh about the behaviour of their child. It is for those who are worried, who are unsure about whether their child's behaviour is normal or whether it indicates that he has something wrong with him. If you are a teacher, it will be helpful to you, too, I hope. Perhaps the behaviour of a particular child is proving very disruptive. You may have always regarded him as a problem child, or you may have noticed that from being bright and lively he has gradually changed into a daydreamer—sad and solitary. Conversely, he may have suddenly become aggressive or hostile, or unwilling to concentrate on his work or comply with your requests. He may have been involved in an extremely serious incident which was completely out of character.

Despite your efforts to cope with him nothing appears to change the way he presently responds.

When they are anxious about the behaviour of a child, both parents and professionals such as teachers often blame themselves for his behaviour. As a parent you will be particularly concerned about the part you may have played in creating the present situation. You may feel that your child's behaviour is a reflection of your own inadequacies, that you are to blame for his present unhappiness. You may have feelings of shame and guilt, even to the extent of now regretting having brought him into the world.

You should never feel like this. While you have undoubtedly done all you could to help your child behave appropriately, don't forget that he is unique, and separate from you. He has his own personality and a special combination of strengths and weaknesses.

And you are not alone in having to cope with a very difficult child. Approximately 7 per cent of pre-school children exhibit problems described by professionals as moderate to marked in severity, and another 15 per cent have 'mild' problems. In other words, one in five is likely to have some kind of disorder. The parents of these younger children principally worry about their restless, disturbed behaviour. They describe their children as attention-seeking and very difficult to manage. Other common concerns are bed-wetting and wetting during the day, sleeplessness and food fads. Of lesser frequency are poor concentration, severe temper tantrums and general anxiety and unhappiness.

The same proportion of children experience problems during adolescence: approximately 10–15 per cent have clearly defined disorders, and another 6 per cent have less apparent difficulties. But the problems most frequently encountered at this age are different from those experienced by younger children; in adolescents there is a predominance of emotional disorders (anxiety disorders and depression), conduct disorders, or a mixture of both.

Childhood disorders are therefore quite common—but, regrettably, not usually noticed soon enough. Parents and teachers often prefer to ignore a child's difficulties, referring to them as a 'passing phase' rather than facing the fact that he may have a psychological problem or—worse—a psychiatric disorder. It is often not until something serious occurs that parents or teachers accept that the child in question needs help. Underlying problems may only come to light when, for example, he or she runs away, attempts to commit suicide or attacks a teacher.

Often the child's condition is simply left to deteriorate, resulting in some instances in a fatal conclusion. So much do we fear the stigma of mind/brain-related health problems that we are willing to sacrifice the happiness and physical well-being of our children: it is estimated that of those children suffering significant personal problems, only one in ten is receiving professional help. Whether you are a parent or a teacher you should therefore be congratulated on casting aside prejudice in the interests of the child and on having the courage and initiative to examine his behaviour more objectively.

If your child is behaving badly there is every chance that he is suffering inside, and that his physical, intellectual and emotional performance is being impaired. You will no doubt have heard of depression, and know that older children in particular may suffer from this; you may have heard of AD/HD—attention-deficit/

hyperactivity disorder—a condition in which a child is unable to concentrate and is exhaustingly impulsive and overactive. But you may be unaware that a child who continually lies and plays truant could be considered by specialists to have a form of conduct disorder (CD), or that an extremely annoying child who continually argues and loses his temper could be seen as having oppositional defiant disorder (ODD). We shall be looking at these and other disorders later.

The purpose of classifying children's behaviour in this way is to enable specialists not only to understand and help the children themselves, but to suggest strategies for those who live and work with them. If you are a parent who is drained and exhausted by anxiety for her son, or a teacher who dreads going to work because of the disruption a certain child may cause, it could help enormously to consider his behaviour as symptomatic of a recognised condition. By doing this you may feel less responsible for his behaviour, more detached, and in a stronger position of control. You may then adopt far more effective measures than, for example, telling the child who is depressed that what he needs is a 'kick up the pants', or threatening the child with conduct disorder that you will have him put behind bars or handed over to the Social Services.

COULD HE BE SUFFERING FROM A DISORDER?

Common problems

To begin with, it is important to recognise that each child is unique not only in his physical makeup but in the way he behaves. He is different from others from the time he is born. He has his own personality and temperament.

If you have a very small child and are concerned that, for example, he appears to smile less and cry more than other children, or fail to 'connect' with others, bear in mind that this may simply be a reflection of his personality, and don't automatically assume that there is something wrong with him. If he fails to respond to soothing in the same way as other children, or is very quiet and subdued or extremely active, it is not necessarily an indication that he has a disorder. If your child is a little older and is afraid of the dark or of strange objects, or of being left on his own, or if his pattern of sleep is irregular or he appears to be excessively fussy about his food, it may be that this is a temporary phase. From time to time all children display one or more of these characteristics. They may simply be reacting and adjusting to the circumstances around them. Similarly, if you have noticed that your teenager is excessively moody or rebellious, be wary of immediately concluding that this is abnormal behaviour. During adolescence children need to make intensive readjustments as they cope with rapid physical and psychological growth. They often become anxious, full of self-doubt and conflict. They may appear hostile, impulsive, angry, and alienated from the adult world.

So how can you tell whether your child's difficulties are significant? How do you know that they are not simply an expression of his individual temperament or of his general development? How can you be sure that you are not overreacting to his behaviour?

What is a disorder?

Assessing whether a child is suffering from a disorder is an extremely complex process which can only be undertaken by highly trained professionals. If you are at all concerned about the behaviour of your child, consult your doctor, who will refer you for specialist help. Many specialists believe that there is no hard line to be drawn between the behaviour of a 'normal' child and that of a child with a disorder. They see the behaviour of children with a disorder differing from that of a normal child only in that it is more *severe and persistent and socially disabling*. Many feel that it is more important to deal with symptoms rather than to worry about labels (see Chapter 4).

We have already mentioned a number of common childhood problems. For most children these present temporary difficulties. For some, however, the problems are so severe and persistent that they become grossly unhappy, unable to learn from their mistakes and incapable of developing meaningful relationships with others. When you are considering whether your child may have some kind of disorder, ask yourself whether his worrying behaviour is so severe and persistent that he could be described as socially disabled.

The following questions may also help you. Your answers may prove useful when you are discussing your child's problems with his teachers, the doctor or other specialists. If your response to one or more of these questions is a definite 'Yes!', then it is likely that your child needs help. But *it may or may not* indicate that he is suffering from a significant disorder.

I must emphasise that there is a wide range of childhood disorders and that they often occur in complex combinations; furthermore, diagnosis is extremely complicated and can only be undertaken by specialists. Whatever your response to these questions, don't hesitate to seek professional advice if you have a persistent, nagging concern. Bear in mind also that because of the limitations of this book I may not have included the kind of question that could prove to be significant for *your* child.

Twenty questions

Consistent features of his behaviour

Q Does my child appear grossly and persistently unhappy?

A He is *consistently* at odds with himself and *persistently* unhappy.

Q Does my child appear lethargic, withdrawn and uninterested in the world around him?

A He is consistently quiet, withdrawn and in his own world.

Q Does my child appear to be overactive?

A He *consistently* has excessive and unlimited energy. He is always restless.

Q Is there a consistent pattern of excessive 'highs' and 'lows' in my child's mood and behaviour?

A He is either excessively withdrawn and unhappy or noticeably euphoric. There is little in between. You have noticed this pattern several times.

Q Does my child's behaviour appear to be excessively impulsive and uninhibited?

A He *consistently* lives according to his impulses. He requires immediate gratification and appears excessively selfish. His 'temper tantrums' appear to be more than what is usually understood by that term.

Q Does my child seem far more immature than others of his age?

A He *consistently* reacts and behaves as would a much younger, or much older, child. In this way his behaviour is grossly inappropriate.

Q Is my child unable to modify or control his behaviour?

A He is *consistently* unable to change his behaviour, or does not appear to have developed any coping strategies (e.g., turning to an alternative activity such as reading a book or going out to play football so as to alleviate the situation in which he finds himself). He does not appear to learn from previous experiences.

Q Does my child's behaviour occur in all situations?

A He behaves in the same worrying manner whether he is at school, at home or elsewhere.

Unusual behaviour

Q Has there been a sudden change in my child's behaviour or mood?

A You have noticed a marked change in the behaviour and attitude of your child. You can think of nothing that has recently happened that could have caused this.

Q Has my child been involved in a serious one-off incident?

A He has been involved in an incident that is so serious, bizarre or outrageous that it could be regarded as a sign of abnormality. He may have set your house on fire, run away or been involved in a robbery. He may have suddenly and inexplicably acted strangely or said something unacceptable and completely out of character. He may have injured himself by, for example, lacerating his arms or taking an overdose of medication or drugs.

(Although most disorders are usually detected by observing behaviour over a period of time, serious one-off incidents may indicate disturbance.)

Q Does my child regularly tell lies, steal, disobey or destroy property?

A He will not do as he is told. He frequently lies to you, steals from you or from others, and destroys property belonging to others including yourself.

His inner thoughts

Q Does my child have worries that consistently intrude into his other thoughts?

A He is *consistently* troubled by worries that obstruct and deflect his thinking.

Q Does my child persistently express concerns that appear to have no foundation?

A He persistently worries about things without any reason for doing so. He may for, example, be constantly concerned that his pet is going to die or that you are going to leave him, when there has never been any indication that you might do so.

Q Does my child have delusions or hallucinate?

A He feels that the whole world is his enemy. He feels worthless and imagines that there is a conspiracy against him.
He insists that he is physically ill when he is in good health.
He believes that he does not exist or, conversely, that he is in a position of great power.
He has described voices or visions that appear to be hallucinations. In general they occur during the waking day and not when he is in bed.
There is no indication that he has taken hallucinatory or toxic drugs, or that he has been involved in religious ritual.

(Hallucinations that occur either just before he falls asleep or just before he wakes up may not be regarded as significant, and in most circumstances neither would his imaginary friends or personal fantasies.)

Q Has my child complained of feeling somehow different, that things seem unreal or that he feels detached from the world around him?

A He complains that he feels that he has changed or that he sees the world as if in a dream. He feels detached from everything, possibly even his own body. He may also have hallucinations.

The effect of his behaviour

Q Does my child's behaviour provoke negative reactions in others?

A He *consistently* aggravates or disturbs others and is unable to form friendships. He is grossly unpopular with his peers. Adults are uneasy or unsettled in his presence.

Q Does my child's behaviour restrict his social life?

A His behaviour *consistently* prevents him from joining in with others either in informal groups (e.g., parties) or formal groups (e.g., clubs, societies). He tends to 'destroy' social gatherings by being excessively overactive, or annoying, or miserable, or withdrawn.

Q Does my child's behaviour seriously affect relationships within our family and restrict our friendships?

A He adversely affects the relationship between you and your partner. He is unable to relate positively to his brothers or sisters. Tensions and conflicts appear to centre on him. You think you have lost friends because of his persistently unacceptable or inappropriate behaviour.

Q Is my child's education suffering because of his behaviour?

A He is unable to concentrate or remember. He either dreams his time away or is regarded as very disruptive. He is unable to form friendships and is either ignored or actively disliked. He has fallen well behind in his schoolwork. He hates going to school and avoids doing so whenever possible.

Q Is he unmanageable?

A Despite all your efforts your child continues to behave inappropriately. He appears to be unable to adjust in any significant way. You are beginning to have a feeling of helplessness and despair because you are no longer able to help or control him.

IS HE MAD OR BAD?

Your child's behaviour may be so persistently demanding and unchangeable that you have come to the conclusion that he must be either mad or bad. In times past, a child who presented severe behavioural problems might have been thought to be possessed by the devil, or he might have been regarded as insane and placed in a 'madhouse', an asylum or a workhouse. His abnormal behaviour might even have been attributed to such bizarre notions as a worm entering his heart, or to masturbation.

Fortunately, we now take a more reasoned, objective approach! Our society is more child-orientated, and advances in biological and behavioural sciences enable us to tackle behavioural problems in a positive, forward-looking way. If your child has a serious behavioural problem it is far more productive to accept that he may have a 'condition' than to think, for example, that he is possessed by the devil. If his condition can be diagnosed and his behaviour accurately described, everyone will be in a better position to help him. Moreover, adopting this approach will certainly help *you* to take more pleasure in him. Much of your present hurt and anguish may be caused by the thought that your child is deliberately and consciously behaving badly.

Focus on thinking of him as being incompetent—disabled–rather than deliberately non-compliant. At the moment, it could be that he is unable to help himself.

COULD HE BE BRAIN-DAMAGED?

Complications during pregnancy and birth

There may have been complications during your pregnancy, or during the birth of your child, that have led you to think that his or her problems are the result of brain damage. But experts who have examined the possibility of links between brain damage during pregnancy or birth and psychiatric disorders have reached no definite conclusions. It would seem that while a child who is brain-damaged stands a greater risk of developing a psychiatric problem, there is no conclusive evidence to suggest that disorders are caused by brain damage. Many children with brain disorders do not have psychiatric problems, and the majority of those who do are free from brain damage.

So it would be unwise to automatically assume that your badly behaved child is 'brain-damaged'.

Head injuries

Establishing the link between head injuries and disorders is complicated by the fact that children—boys in particular—who are excessively overactive are more likely to be involved in accidents and to suffer head injuries. The disorder could therefore be seen as being present before the injury, or indeed as causing it. A child's pre-injury characteristics also affect the chances of his developing a serious disorder after an accident. He will be at greater risk of doing so if previously he had emotional and behavioural problems.

However, severe head injury can in some instances alter a child's behaviour. He may become socially disinhibited; he may be outspoken, ask embarrassing questions, make very personal comments or get undressed in inappropriate circumstances; he may become forgetful, over-talkative, impulsive, or careless about his cleanliness and appearance. It is worth noting that children who suffer head injuries are less likely to develop psychiatric problems if, following the accident, their parents do not become overprotective. They have a natural tendency to do so, of course, but it often means that they fail to deal effectively with the child's behaviour. Because of his injury, they resist disciplining him.

Many behavioural difficulties which follow a head injury prove to be temporary; to avoid them becoming anything more than this, it is important that as far as discipline goes the sooner things 'get back to normal' the better.

Brain dysfunction
It is generally accepted that in some children the brain does not work as it should. Hyperactivity, impulsivity and inhibition disorders are thought to be caused by faulty neurotransmitters—brain chemicals which relay the myriad messages controlling our responses. In these cases, the brain is not damaged, but neither is it working as efficiently as it should. The behaviour of some children who have these particular conditions can be improved dramatically when the neurotransmitters are helped to work by medication.

DOES HE HAVE A MENTAL DISABILITY?

The severity of your child's behavioural problems may have made you wonder whether he could have a mental disability. If he has, in addition to his behavioural problems, he will show clear signs that he has limited academic ability and a limited capacity to work. He will also have difficulty in communicating with and relating to others, in looking after himself, in safely existing in the community, and in generally directing his own life.

The more intelligent the child, the less chance is there that he will suffer from a disorder, but those in the higher ability range are just as likely as others to have emotional problems. At the other end of the scale, those children who have a mild mental disability are three to four times more likely to suffer from a psychiatric disorder, and consequent behavioural problems, than children in general. Amongst those who are described as having a severe mental disability, approximately 50 per cent will have a significant disorder. Children with mental disabilities who have disorders commonly suffer from hyperactivity and severe communication problems including repetitive and seemingly purposeless activities—such as mannerisms, rocking, hand-flapping—and self-injury.

SHOULD I SEARCH FOR A LABEL? (See Chapter 4)

You may have reservations about labelling children. You may think that if a child is labelled he is likely to live up to the image or to use it as an excuse for his behaviour. You may fear that it will stigmatise him. But if you want to move forward from your present position you are going to have to take some risks. Besides, how can his behaviour deteriorate further? Or, to put it another way, how much more anxious can you get?

I imagine, in fact, that much of your present anxiety stems from your never having been able to get to the root of your child's problems—and that you are already, perhaps unwittingly, searching for a label for his behaviour.

Perhaps you feel that if you can find a label that describes his condition there will be a chance of discovering a cure, and that even if a cure is not available an accurate assessment will make it easier for you to know what to do about it. This would be a sensible approach, for in addition to being offered expert advice on how to deal with their child, parents can get a great deal of help from parent support groups, which exist throughout the country and cover a wide range of childhood problems (see Appendix A), and teachers can benefit from the increasing body of professional knowledge related to specific disorders. The child himself, of course, will also benefit if his condition is diagnosed, in that he will have a better chance of getting extra, and more appropriate, help.

Paradoxically, knowing that your child has a disorder may prove to be a burden off your mind: you may feel reassured by the knowledge that his behaviour is not entirely due to the way in which you as a parent have brought him up, or, as a teacher, have taught him. How often have you felt the finger being pointed at *you* when *he* has upset someone? How often have *you* lain awake at night feeling guilty and inadequate because *he* has disrupted your classroom?

Later we shall be looking at how you might help your child to cope with his condition. For the moment, you may be encouraged to know that experts are increasingly reasserting the part that nature plays in determining the ways in which we think, learn and behave. A child behaving badly is not always, or only, the result of ineffective parenting or poor teaching.

If you have any remaining doubts about labelling, do bear in mind that labels are only devised to help us communicate. As far as disorders go, they are convenient ways of describing clusters of behaviour and of helping experts to research them and recommend treatment. Labels are far from 'absolute', and although some are easier to define than others there is a considerable overlap between them. It is common for a child to display symptoms of a variety of disorders. The specialist has to decide which, if any, predominates.

It is particularly important to remember this and not to become frustrated when specialists cannot provide an immediate and conclusive definition of your child's condition. It will help if you think of diagnosis and treatment programmes as being exploratory: much will be accomplished through trial and error. It will also help if you think of yourself as part of the exploration team. How close you come to accurately describing your child's behaviour will depend on the understanding and enthusiasm of each team member.

WILL HIS BEHAVIOUR EVER IMPROVE?

Until you have consulted a specialist and are more sure of the nature of your child's problem, you will not be able to estimate the chances of his behaviour improving. But what *can* be said is that, although a great deal of research still needs to be done, the indications are that if a child has a serious disorder at a young age there is, regrettably, a distinct possibility that he will experience a disorder in later life.

If your child is suffering from some form of depression (p. 112) or from schizophrenia (p. 114), he is likely to be at risk in the long term. If at a young age he is described as having a conduct disorder (p. 62), and this is associated with hyperactivity or inattention as well as poor peer relationships, he will probably develop a personality disorder during adulthood. If he has autistic features (p. 74), these will almost certainly remain with him and he will never be a fully functioning adult. If your child is suffering from an anxiety disorder (p. 94) he is likely to have some kind of emotional problems when he is an adult.

The form of a disorder may change between childhood and adolescence. For example, a specific developmental language disorder in early childhood may disappear, then later take the form of a specific learning difficulty (especially in relation to reading—p. 87). A young child may have an animal phobia (p. 97—e.g. fear of dogs) whereas an adolescent is more likely to have a social phobia (p. 99) such as agoraphobia or school phobia.

The future for a child with a disorder may therefore appear rather bleak. But you should not despair. Much depends on the nature and severity of your child's condition. As I said earlier, childhood conditions are complex in the way they present, and nothing can be certain. After discussing your child's behaviour with a professional, you may discover that problems which presently appear to be insoluble are *not* in fact symptoms of a serious disorder. You may discover that his behaviour can be considerably alleviated by adjustments at home and at school or by medication.

Whatever the situation, you will be in a better position to help your child if you think in terms of coping rather than curing. If he does have a disorder, it is unlikely that he is going to be completely cured. His problems are either going to persist in their present form, or change as he grows older. Prospects for the future will be considerably brighter if you are able to help him appreciate his difficulties, whether mild or severe, and if you can help him to learn how to live with them.

CONCLUSION

If you are at all worried about your child's behaviour, don't hesitate to seek professional advice.

Perhaps you have a very young child who appears persistently unhappy and hard to placate. On the other hand, he may be excessively active, demanding and restless. Or you may have an older child who is clearly having problems at school. He may be falling behind with his work; his teachers may have told you either that he is very quiet and withdrawn, or that he is regularly antagonising other children and causing disruption because of his inability to sit still, focus on the matter in hand and generally conform. Or you may have a teenaged child who has been involved in a number of serious incidents. Perhaps he has suddenly become uninterested in everything, or begun to act in a strange way.

These are just some of the problems experienced by most children from time to time, but in others they can be an indication of a disorder that needs specialist attention.

* * *

In this chapter we have posed questions that many parents ask themselves when their child's behaviour simply becomes too much for them to tolerate. These questions may have prompted you to take action—indeed, you should not hesitate to do so if you are still worried. Many parents resist seeking advice. They harbour their fears in the hope that the child's behaviour will begin to right itself. They are afraid of the stigma that could be attached to him if he is described as having a condition. They also feel that they themselves would be stigmatised. As a result their child continues to suffer.

We shall deal with some of the issues surrounding the feelings you have for your child in the next chapter. It is worth noting here, though, that when parents are told that their child has a condition they invariably do feel relieved. They are able to shed the guilt that they have previously felt, and are significantly more able to help him. Similarly, when teachers are informed of a child's condition they begin to have more realistic expectations of him. They become less frustrated with his behaviour, and deal with him more effectively.

And when the child becomes aware of his condition, he may for the first time take a step back from his behaviour and begin to assume a position of control.

2 Am I to Blame for My Child's Behaviour?

The behaviour of your child may be so demanding that you are continually anxious and exhausted. You may only be able to relax and be yourself when she is not with you, and even then you are on edge, wondering what she might be doing. And if you are this particular child's teacher, the thought of her being in your class group may fill you with apprehension and make what is otherwise a pleasurable occupation an absolute nightmare.

You may find that you are drawn into adopting her negative and belligerent manner. When her behaviour becomes intolerable you may shout at her to 'smarten up' or to 'stop being stupid'. You may tell her that she is idle, or frequently refer to her as a 'pain in the backside'. On the other hand, if she is quiet, unresponsive and 'flat' you may no longer pay her any attention. You may even have told her that if *she* isn't bothered about anything, you don't see why you should be.

Difficult children often draw you into their behavioural style in this way, and it is hard to resist expressing your concern with an angry reaction. Their behaviour can be so persistently draining that, as a parent or as a teacher, you soon begin to think that it is you and not the child who has the problem. But if you are to help her you need to remain in control of your feelings and to respond in a different, a more positive, manner.

A way of doing this is to look more closely at how you really feel about her and to examine any underlying worries you may have about yourself and your situation.

HOW DO I FEEL ABOUT HER?

She wears me out

Your child may be so demanding that you are permanently anxious and feel physically and emotionally worn out.

It may ease your anxiety if you recognise that she is an individual in her own right: she has a unique temperament which determines not only the way *she* behaves but the way in which others respond to her. Each child plays a crucial part in the relationship she has with others: her behaviour is not solely determined by those around her. For example, a young child who is hard to soothe will elicit a different reaction from her parents and teachers from one who responds positively; an older child who is negative, uncontrollable and intense will engender a similar response in others.

Given, then, that a child's *temperament* plays a significant part in determining how she behaves and how others perceive her, you cannot be held entirely responsible for her behaviour.

You may feel worn out by your child not only because of her incessant demands or lack of response, but because underneath you are deeply disturbed at your own inability to relate to her in a meaningful way. But it could simply be that she has a particularly 'difficult' temperament and that others, apart from you, also find it hard to cope with her. From birth, some children may be described as 'easy' and others as 'difficult', and difficult children place enormous pressures on those around them. Their parents often feel that they are only able to carry on because of the prospect of the peace that will come when the child eventually goes to sleep—for some, indeed, even this time of the day offers little or no respite. And teachers of these children suffer anxiety symptoms because of their unpredictability and the level of disruption they are likely to cause at any time.

So great is the pressure exerted on them that parents may eventually ignore the child's behaviour and allow her to do as she pleases, and professionals may adopt a contentious attitude to the child and ultimately recommend her exclusion. If you do feel emotionally drained by your child, perhaps it is because you are taking too much responsibility for her behaviour. You are feeling unnecessarily guilty for what *she* does. If you can think of her more as separate from yourself—with each of you having your own needs and responsibilities—you may become less embroiled in her problems. If you can think of her as a child who is experiencing personal inner difficulties, separate from your own, you may not feel so anxious and so exhausted by her behaviour.

Needless to say, if you are feeling as 'drained' as I have

described it would be wise to have a medical check-up. Bear in mind that if you have a particularly worrisome child it is easy to assume that she is the cause of your problems and ignore the possibility that you yourself are ill. Your doctor may be able to suggest a course of action for both of you if you explain exactly what you feel the problem is.

She is completely self-centred

You may feel that your child is utterly selfish, that she thinks that the whole world revolves around her, and that no one else matters—except when she wants something from them. If she makes you feel like this, it could be that you do indeed spend all your time meeting her needs—and at great expense: you may have begun to lose sight of yourself as a person in your own right. It is natural to want to do all you can for your child, but easy to fall into the trap of living only for her.

You must never forget that you too are an individual with your own particular needs. Focusing on the fact that her behaviour is a reflection of an inner condition will help, but you must also examine your own lifestyle. We shall discuss how you might do this in Chapter 7, but for the time being it may be worth asking yourself what interests you have in life, and how you presently pursue them. If the answer is 'none', it's time to take action.

As a teacher, you may resent the amount of time spent with the 'difficult' child and the fact that the threat of disruption permeates your classroom. In Chapter 8 we shall discuss measures that you can adopt to alleviate this situation, but for the moment consider whether you focus enough on planning for her, or whether you regard her exceptional needs as secondary to those of the rest of your group. If you begin by seeing her needs as the priority, and then pre-plan with this in mind, you may find that the rest of the class operates smoothly.

It can help both teachers and parents to interpret the behaviour of a 'selfish' child as a measure of weakness: the child may be over-demanding because she needs reassurance; the parent may see the child as selfish because of his own weakness; the child may appear to be selfish in the classroom because of inadequate forward planning by the teacher.

She is an absolute nuisance

You may, of course, as a parent, feel that your child is a nuisance because she is preventing you from pursuing some very strong personal interests that you have always had and that you feel keep you going. If this *is* the way you see her, perhaps you should ask yourself whether you have got the balance right between fulfilling your own needs and meeting hers. It may prove fruitful to consider whether you have made adequate arrangements to avoid your child feeling unwanted while you are enjoying yourself. If you haven't, she will behave even worse so as to gain your attention.

Make sure that you have recruited friends to help you with your child and that you have a scheduled special time allocated for her when you are at home. Talk to her about your interests—be enthusiastic about them—and at the same time, of course, encourage her to tell you about hers.

As her teacher, you might be able to avoid regarding her as a nuisance if you bear in mind that, while the majority of your class may be able to work on their own, the difficult child will undoubtedly need special attention. See the need to cater for her as a priority—don't let it be an afterthought, or regard it as an unwelcome burden.

She is a total embarrassment

If you are embarrassed by the behaviour of your child it may be that deep down you feel that it reflects all *your* worst points. This will inevitably be the case if you have low self-esteem: the solution is, again, to focus on fulfilling yourself rather more than you are at present. Find interests and socialise, so that you can begin to feel more fulfilled, and recognise your better qualities. If you can see these more clearly in yourself you will begin to see them reflected in your child.

As I have already stressed, there is a need for many parents to see themselves more as separate persons in their own right: embarrassment may be caused by living too much under their child's skin, doing too much feeling for her and trying to lead *her* life rather than their own. One way of avoiding embarrassment is to share your concerns—rather than always be fighting your child's corner—with those friends and neighbours who are likely to encounter her behaviour. If they are aware of her difficulties and of your worries, they are more likely to be supportive—and any embarrassment will be put in perspective.

As her teacher, bear in mind that research indicates that children often mirror the behaviour of their teacher. If you are anxious, your anxiety may be reflected in your pupils—and more so in those who are particularly vulnerable. The feeling of tension and unease that teachers have when dealing with a difficult child is perhaps caused by an underlying feeling of guilt and embarrassment at not having the necessary skills to control the child or motivate her to learn. If you feel this way, bear in mind that because of the nature of a 'difficult' child there will always be instances where she is unable to conform. A great deal of unease and embarrassment can be avoided if everyone who is working with her is aware of her condition—in this respect the value of referring her to a specialist as early as possible can be appreciated.

She is a thorough disappointment

If you regard your child as a disappointment, it may be that you have always had false expectations of her. All parents have a mental picture of how they would like themselves and their children to be, but the more rigid your idea of a model child, the greater your chance of being disappointed. If you do have unfounded expectations of your child—if what you would like her to be is beyond her capabilities—not only will you be disappointed in her but you may see a deterioration in her behaviour. Difficult children tend to be more sensitive to the feelings of others, and if they know that you are deeply disappointed in them they will express their frustration with even more inappropriate behaviour.

Is it possible that the disappointment you feel in your child may be a reflection of your own sense of failure in life? If you are unhappy with your lot, there is a good chance that you may unconsciously inflict your disappointment on her. As far as your own life goes it may help to take a close look at your ideal model—what you seem always to aspire to—and assess this in relation to what you know is realistically possible. Consider accepting yourself for what you are rather than condemning yourself for what you are not.

As far as your attitude to your child goes, imagine, for example, that instead of having behavioural problems she had epilepsy.

Would your attitude to her be any different? Could you ever describe her as a disappointment? Remember that if she is suffering from a disorder she is in fact disabled—disabled in a different way than if she had epilepsy, but none the less disabled.

If you feel you could, perhaps it is because you are not yet convinced that she might be unable to control her behaviour. Perhaps you remain convinced that she *can* control herself, but is choosing not to do so; you still feel that she has unlocked potential that she refuses to use. The problem is that if you maintain this stance you will make little progress with her, because you will be starting from a position of criticism and rejection rather than one of appreciation and acceptance. She may indeed have great potential, but if this is to be realised you need to give her your support.

As this child's teacher you too may feel that she is not fulfilling her potential—that her intelligence is not reflected in her academic work. You may put this down to laziness, implying once again that she is quite capable of doing well—if she wants to. To avoid transmitting a sense of disappointment to the child and a consequent escalation of her problems, put the question of whether she might have a disorder at the top of your list, rather than persisting with a subjective assessment of her work.

There is a strong relationship between a child's performance and the expectations of her parents and teachers.

HAS SHE INHERITED MY BAD POINTS?

Genetics

As her parent you may have a nagging suspicion that you yourself were just like she is when you were a child, or you may catch glimpses in her behaviour of the darker side of her father or of some other relative. As her teacher, you may think that the child is just like her older brothers or sisters whom you have previously taught. In other words, you may imagine that she has inherited her behaviour, that her problems are genetic.

While there is evidence to support the notion that some disorders are inherited, particularly in the case of persistent and severe ones, there are too many other influences on a child's development to simply say, 'It's in her genes.' For example, a child who is described as having a conduct disorder (p. 62) may have been influenced by delinquent friends, or the condition may be the result of her hyperactivity, or it may be related to traumatic events occurring in her family.

Trying to decide whether a child has inherited her condition is also complicated by the fact that the mental health of her parents may be affecting her (see My Depression . . . ?, below, and Involvement in Crime?, p. 26). If a parent is suffering from depression (see Appendix B) or schizophrenia (see Appendix B), her child too may have a significant disorder—but this may be the result of the parent's inability to deal with the child rather than the child having a particular genetic makeup.

A further complication is that a child will invariably suffer from more than one condition. For instance, if she is described as having attention-deficit/hyperactivity disorder (see Appendix B and p. 59) she may also display symptoms of conduct disorder (see Appendix B and p. 62) and have significant reading difficulties.

Establishing genetic links for specific conditions is therefore not easy. While research does seem to be pointing to the likelihood that disorders have a genetic base, in most instances the links have not been irrefutably established. For the moment it would seem realistic to say that, while most disorders are not exactly inherited, because of their genetic makeup some children may be more predisposed to disorders than others—more vulnerable to the effects of any adverse circumstances in which they may find themselves.

If you feel that your child *has* inherited her condition, don't think that this means that she is untreatable: adjustments can be made to alleviate the condition even of those children who are suffering from the small number of conditions that are more clearly genetic in origin. The complexities are such that, rather than speculate on genetic origin, it is much more productive to look at your child's actual behaviour and consider whether any adjustments can be made at home or at school to help her cope with her condition. We are a long way from tampering with the genetic makeup of a child in order to alter her behaviour, either in a practical or an ethical sense.

My depression, other disorder, or illness?

If you yourself suffer from some kind of disorder or illness, your child will be at greater risk of having behavioural problems. This is not to imply that she has inherited your illness: she may simply be suffering from the consequences. For example, if you suffer from depression you may be unable to communicate effectively with her. You may not have the energy to discipline and control her as you know you should. You may have become less involved, and you may have distanced yourself from her. If your illness or condition is severe, you may have even completely rejected her. On the other hand, you may have tried to compensate for your inadequacies by becoming overprotective.

If your child is very young, your behaviour will confuse her and she will become distressed; if she is older she may not appreciate why you behave as you do, and become resentful. The children of mothers who are depressed are often shy, isolated and withdrawn or, conversely, destructive, defiant, impatient, uncooperative, belligerent and socially isolated. Many have problems with their peers and with their schoolwork.

A high percentage of people who are suffering from some form of disorder know that they are ineffective as parents. If you feel that your personal problems are preventing you from doing all you can for your child, do seek help. But don't assume that if you have a disorder or illness your child is *automatically* suffering. Although children of depressed parents have a greater risk of developing behavioural difficulties, not all do so. A great deal depends on the severity of their parent's condition and on whether there is another effective parent or other adult in the home.

Of great significance is the level of the child's self-esteem. If your child relates well to others and is successful at school, she may not only be unaffected by your condition but, if she is made aware of it, she may be able to help you to cope more effectively.

If you want to minimise the effect of your disorder on your child, do make sure that you are not only receiving treatment but that you are being open and honest with her and with others about your difficulties. Together you may be able to devise effective practical strategies. The least you will do by explaining will be to avoid your child misinterpreting your behaviour and, as a consequence, behaving badly. Bear in mind that she will sense that there is a problem, and that she will worry less if she knows what it is.

If, as a teacher, you are aware that a 'difficult' child's parents have personal problems, you will be able to support her by providing opportunities for her to privately express her concerns. If you can arrange a 'social' visit to her home, that will make your support even more effective.

Involvement in crime

If you or your partner have been convicted of crimes and could be regarded as persistent offenders, there is every likelihood that your child may have a disorder. While it is not firmly established that juvenile delinquents have inherited their traits, it is generally accepted that all children model themselves on their parents. Similarly, if members of your family take drugs, are alcoholics or exhibit antisocial behaviour, you should not be surprised if your child does the same.

The children of criminals are under a great deal of stress. They usually have to cope with a high level of conflict between their parents, who may constantly quarrel and be physically and emotionally abusive and violent. Because of deep-seated personal problems, such parents are unable to provide their children with the discipline and guidance they need. If a child does something wrong, they may regard it as relatively unimportant or even normal. As a result, they fail to reprimand him.

Of course, if your child is involved in crime it does not necessarily mean that you or your partner have criminal tendencies. You may live in a neighbourhood where there is a large and influential gang of delinquents, and it may be that your child has been unable to resist becoming involved. His problems may also, of course, be rooted in his condition. For example, unknown to you he may have always suffered from attention-deficit/hyperactivity disorder. He may, because of this, have been unable to concentrate at school and fallen behind with his work. Then, as a consequence, he may have been rejected by his peers and become antisocial. In this way he may have drifted into delinquency and crime.

If you are the teacher of a child who appears to be delinquent, don't assume that he has inherited his problem—consider the greater likelihood that he is reacting to severe adverse influences. Be aware, too, that a child's disorder can lead to 'secondary' problems such as alienation and delinquency. If you fail to detect his problems at an early stage, he may ultimately become alienated from society. You can help him by ensuring that there are always opportunities for him to discuss any problems that he may be experiencing.

HAS SOMETHING HAPPENED TO MAKE HER LIKE THIS?

You may be wondering whether something specific has happened to make your child behave so badly. You may reflect that her behaviour suddenly changed for the worse after a particular incident.

A serious accident, incident or disaster?

If your child has witnessed or been involved in a serious accident or incident, or in a disaster of some sort, she will inevitably react in some way. But each child reacts differently to stressful situations—while some have a natural resilience that helps them through, others are more vulnerable.

Children who have been close to a major incident in which, for example, they have witnessed violence, may be unable to sleep. They may have vivid flashbacks to the incident, develop a fear of the dark or have nightmares. They may become very irritable and anxious and find it hard to separate from their parents. In school they may have difficulty concentrating because of frightening memories which repeatedly intrude into their thoughts. If they have witnessed death, they may feel a loss of faith in the future; their priorities may change and they may appear to live only for the moment.

These are just a few of the reactions that children may have to a traumatic event. The degree to which they are affected depends on the severity of the incident, how far they were involved in it and how life-threatening it appeared to them. Another significant factor is how far the trauma was deliberately perpetrated. If, for instance, a child is present during a deliberate and fatal attack by one person on another she will suffer considerably more distress than a child who witnesses a fatal road accident.

A child who is exposed to a serious incident or disaster will usually recover, but the lasting effect on her will depend on the seriousness of the event and the degree of support that she experiences around her. Young children who have suffered such trauma will often not bother their parents with their consequent anxieties; adolescents, even though they may think that they are going mad because of the stress, will often prefer not to tell anyone of their difficulties. For these reasons it is common for both parents and teachers to underplay the lasting effects of a traumatic event: when asked, they may comment that the child doesn't appear to have been too badly affected. But it has been found that when children are given the opportunity to share their thoughts and feelings with an adult outside their immediate family, they often retell the incident in detail and gain an obvious sense of relief in the telling.

A child's reaction to a stressful episode can last for many years and be extremely disabling for her. If you feel that your child may have suffered from a traumatic event more than she wants you to know, it would clearly be a good idea to arrange for her to talk to a trained independent counsellor.

Illness?

If a child has suffered a serious illness at an early age or been in hospital because of an accident, she may develop emotional and behavioural problems. These can occur close to the time of the illness, or much later in life. Long-term illnesses, too, create behavioural problems for many children: for example, those who suffer from diabetes have particular difficulty in coping with their illness. A child may also be affected in the same way by the serious illness of a brother, sister or parent.

How far a child is affected by illness or hospitalisation will depend on her age and how much she is able to understand and cope with her condition. It will also depend on whether her parents or others are able to provide her with support and how well they can communicate with her. As with other traumatic experiences, an effective approach is to discuss the child's feelings about the event with her and, in the case of an ongoing illness, how she might come to terms with it.

As a parent, you too may need this kind of help. Many parents become very distressed when their child has a serious illness or has had to undergo extensive hospital treatment because of an accident—especially if it has occurred in the home and resulted, for instance, in a burn or scald—for which they feel responsible.

If you are a teacher, it will be useful to know of any significant illnesses that a child may have had in the past and which may be at the root of her present behavioural problems. It is essential, of course, always to be aware of any current medical condition that she may have.

My divorce?

You may have separated or divorced from your partner and be wondering how much this has affected your child's behaviour.

It is undoubtedly the case that children of parents who are separated or divorced experience difficulties. While very young ones may appear not to understand what is happening, they are finely tuned into their parents' emotions and can become quite distressed. Not only are they often exposed to heated exchanges and heightened emotions, but they can suffer in the very real way caused by their warring parents, under great stress, being unable to care for them properly. Older children may copy the way in which their parents relate to each other, and become hostile and aggressive. Adolescents, striving towards adulthood, may develop psychological problems and become involved in alcohol or substance abuse.

Problems don't necessarily occur at the actual time of the separation or divorce. It is often the case that a child has already been having problems for some time—problems perhaps caused by a long-standing antagonism between the parents. This *may* indicate that it is better for the child to live with a happy, lone parent than with two who are constantly at loggerheads. Although this is not proven, it does seem that whether a child has one parent or two is not as important as being provided with affection, consistent discipline and supervision. If these are on hand, then she will not be placed at such risk, even in stressful situations.

Your child's behavioural problems may also, of course, be rooted in her own personal difficulties. As I have already mentioned, some children are more able than others to cope with their circumstances. While some are resilient, others are fragile, reacting negatively to any degree of instability or change. In some instances their behaviour can be so stressful for parents that a vicious circle develops in which problems continually escalate.

Although all children are adversely affected by divorce or separation, it is almost impossible to accurately assess *how much* they suffer. A great deal depends on the amount of support that they have around them. A child who is thought to be fairly resilient within herself may be badly affected, whereas a child who is regarded as vulnerable may suffer fewer consequences because of a highly effective network of support. If one of her parents can continue to provide her with an effective blend of affection, discipline, consistency and supervision, the risk of her being adversely affected will be minimised. If she has another significant adult in her life—particularly a grandparent—and a good relationship with a brother or sister, she will fare better. If she has one special friend and attends a school that has a positive and structured approach to pupils' family circumstances, her resistance to the stress of divorce will be considerably enhanced.

It is commonly found that following a divorce or separation more problems develop in children when they are placed with a parent of the opposite sex. Boys who remain with their mothers have particular difficulties—possibly related to the loss of a male figure with whom to identify, or in a more practical way to the inability of some mothers to exert the necessary degree of discipline. A consequence of this is that mother and son may begin to interact negatively, and he may become increasingly non-compliant and often aggressive. It is easy to understand how this happens, when one imagines the effect of divorce or separation on a lone parent. Furthermore, a mother on her own may become depressed and unable to cope. She may have been suffering from depression before the divorce, which has now exacerbated her illness. It is not easy for her to provide firm leadership in a situation of such uncertainty. There is a strong link between parental depression, both before and after divorce, and behavioural difficulties in children.

If you are separated or divorced, or contemplating becoming so, it would seem that to minimise the impact on your child you should make sure that you do not prolong the process of separation, that it is amicable, and that you make very clear arrangements for access to the child for whichever of the two of you doesn't have custody. Don't become too dependent on the child for emotional reassurance, and above all convince her that you still care by providing an appropriate blend of warmth and firmness. She needs to know that you are there for her, and, depending on her age, that there is someone in control of her life.

Exposing her to prolonged and excessive strife and uncertainty will have an adverse effect on her—and more especially if she already has problems of her own.

Bereavement

You may feel that your child's present difficulties have been caused by the death of a person who was close to her. It is difficult to make a general assessment of the effect of bereavement on children's behaviour since there are so many other factors to consider, but it is undoubtedly the case that they are affected in some way or other, either in the short term or later in life.

Depending on their age, children think of death in different ways. Pre-school children attach little importance to it, but after the age of five they begin to have some idea of what it might mean. Generally, it is not until they are about nine years old that they begin to accept that death is a fact of life, and show signs of reacting on an emotional level.

But dealing with the death of a parent can present particularly severe problems. A very young child will often become extremely distressed and impossible to console. Later, her sense of loss will turn to despair, and she may become full of grief and apathy. She may appear 'flat' and unresponsive. She may rock herself to and fro for long periods of time. Only when she has accepted that her parent is not going to return will her behaviour improve.

The death of a parent when the child is three or four years old is regarded as particularly significant, because it is at this time that children identify with the parent of the same sex. If a boy loses his father or a girl her mother he or she may experience more severe identity problems later, during adolescence. They may suffer from depression, and boys in particular may become withdrawn or antisocial. Whether the death of a parent will affect a child in later life will to a large extent depend on the amount of support she receives from those who remain with her. For example, if she remains in familiar surroundings with the other parent or another adult who has a good relationship with her the effect may be minimal, but if circumstances dictate that she be placed in an institution with strangers she may be badly affected.

Older children may not react in the same way as younger ones. They are more able to understand and share feelings, and because of their more developed social network they are less dependent on the remaining parent. If the parents were not happy in their relationship, then the death of one of them will have more of an adverse effect on their child. A child will also be affected by the death of one of her parents if the remaining parent finds it hard to cope. And as noted earlier, if that parent is depressed, he or she may withdraw and be unable to offer the child the amount of care she requires.

A lone parent experiences greatly increased pressures. Not only must she come to terms with her grief but she often has to assume full responsibility for the child. In addition to running the home, she may have to work to maintain it. Her grief may permeate the family and considerably diminish her child's happiness. She may become over-reliant on her for emotional support, and unconsciously place too much on her shoulders. The child may, for example, be required to replace the missing partner—by doing all the household chores, looking after her brothers or sisters, or working excessively at evenings or weekends for essential income. A child may, therefore, be affected by the death of a parent in a very practical sense.

Many parents shield their children from death. For instance, they may think that it would serve no good cause to take them to the funeral. Whatever your personal decision may be in respect to this, it is important for the child to complete her mourning process and, whatever her age, not only to come to terms with her inner sense of loss but to appreciate the consequent practicalities.

If you feel that a bereavement may be at the root of your child's problems, provide her with the opportunity to discuss the matter with either yourself or someone outside the family. Some counsellors are specially trained to deal with bereavement. If you feel that *you* have never overcome *your* grief, and that as a consequence you find it impossible to cope with your child's, you too should seek help. If you are unable to unburden yourself to a friend or relative, your local library or family doctor will be able to give you details of counselling facilities in your area.

You need to be strong for your child.

Children who are bereaved in childhood but well adjusted as adults have been found to have had lone parents who were independent, hard-working and energetic. If you are a warm and affectionate person who has been badly affected by the loss of your partner or loved one, or if you are anything but independent and sense a loss of energy and enthusiasm for living, it is in the interests of both you and your child to seek help.

HAS SHE BEEN AFFECTED BY OUR FAMILY CIRCUMSTANCES?

You may feel that your difficult child is reacting to the state of affairs in your family. A lack of money coming into the home may be a constant cause of aggravation, or you may be living in overcrowded conditions that lead to constant arguments and fights, or you or your partner may be suffering from illness or stress.

If circumstances of this kind have been severe and prolonged, and you know that your home has not been a happy one, then your child could have been, or be being, badly affected. The degree to which this may have occurred will depend on the number of problems you are experiencing, and for how long they have persisted. Most children are able to cope with occasional stress, but if they are constantly exposed to a large number of significant, intense problems they are likely to develop long-term chronic disorders. These are some of the particular family situations that have been found to be directly or indirectly related to disorders in children:

1 *A poor relationship between parents can affect a child's sense of security* Parents constantly argue in front of a child. They are abusive towards each other and the children, and *may* become violent. On the other hand, they may be persistently resentful or sullen and never speak. The child exists in an atmosphere of distrust and uncertainty.
2 *Low status in the community can adversely affect the relationship a child has with her peers* Her family has the reputation of being 'neighbours from hell', or her father is seen sweeping the streets. The child is rejected and taunted by her peers.
3 *An overcrowded home often results in frustrations and tensions for the child* Family members get on each other's nerves. Pressures build and crises develop. The child is unable to have her own space—literally and emotionally. It is impossible for her to do her homework. She falls behind and ultimately becomes alienated.
4 *A large family means that a child may not receive the amount of attention she needs, or she may be denied the opportunity to express her feelings* The more emotionally vulnerable child will not be given the necessary extra dose of affection. She will not receive the time she needs to express her thoughts and feelings. In her frustration, she will either strike out at others or withdraw into herself.
5 *The personal problems of the mother or father may be so severe that she or he is unable to care for the child properly* One or both of the parents may be depressed or suffer from schizophrenia. One or both may have a physical

disability. They are unable to provide their child, who herself may be suffering from a disorder, with the care and supervision that she so desperately needs.

6 *If the family is dependent on the state for their survival* Because the parents are unemployed or unemployable the family receives state support. Parents and children have a poor sense of who they are and what they are worth. They have little sense of control over their lives.

7 *If the father is involved in crime* (p. 26).

If a child is exposed to just one of these 'stresses', she may not be too badly affected, but if she is exposed to several there is a high risk of her developing a disorder. As we saw previously, a great deal depends on a child's inner resilience and on whether she has the capacity to cope with the intensity of the situation that she finds herself in. The degree of support that she gets from others (see My Divorce?, p. 29) may also help her to withstand constant stress. But it is doubtful whether any child is able to remain unscathed if she faces a multitude of intensely stressful situations such as those that I have mentioned.

CONCLUSION

Although you may feel that your child's behaviour is so intolerable that she must have a disorder, it is important to recognise that her condition may have been triggered or exacerbated by events and circumstances. Not least will her behaviour depend on your attitude towards her and on the amount of support you are able to provide.

Whether you are a parent living with a difficult child or a teacher working with one, it is important to assess how you feel about her. Over time, her behaviour may have made such great demands on you that you are now able to think of her only in a negative and subjective way. You may have begun to feel that she is simply a totally self-centred and obnoxious child, or one who continually embarrasses you. If she is withdrawn and quiet you may regard her with sadness and disappointment. You may search for reasons for her behaviour and find yourself reflecting on your own inadequacies.

In this chapter you have had the opportunity to consider these issues; hopefully, you will now have begun to regard your child more objectively—and in a more positive light.

You may wonder whether your child's behaviour can be attributed to anything specific in the past, or whether it is just the result of the generally appalling state of affairs that has existed in your family for a very long time. So it may have been useful to examine, as we have in this chapter, how a child may react to events in her life and to the circumstances that surround her. Considering what has occurred in the past may have helped you to appreciate the stressful situations that she has had to endure: you may even marvel at the fact that you have both managed to survive until now! On the other hand, you may have come to the conclusion that your child's circumstances have not been at all traumatic or stressful, and that they could not possibly be the reason why she is behaving so badly. A third possibility is that you may be unaware of things that have happened, or are presently happening, to your child.

In the next chapter we shall consider a number of other reasons for difficult behaviour—ones that are often less obvious to those involved and some that are hidden from parents and teachers by children who suffer in silence.

3 Hidden Problems

When parents or teachers seek help, they often discover that it is not easy to find. This is especially true when a child's behavioural symptoms are not severe or intense. Although professionals are able to recognise the clearer cases of disorder, many fail to notice the milder forms. In addition, there are those who remain reluctant to accept the validity of some behavioural disorders and who, even with severe cases, emphasise that the child's present and previous circumstances are at the root of his problems.

So when you refer your child for professional help, it is important to be well prepared. Whether you are going to discuss his behaviour with his teacher or with the family doctor, or whether you have reached the stage where you are to see a specialist in childhood disorders, he or she will want to know as much as possible about your child's history and his present circumstances. In the first two chapters we have examined the possibility of his having a disorder. We have looked at the way he behaves and how this affects those around him. We have considered the relationship that you have with him and discussed how family circumstances in general may affect a child. We have also noted that the diagnosis of childhood disorders is complex. Specialists need to examine all aspects of the child's life if they are to understand his behaviour.

In this chapter, therefore, we shall take a further look at other reasons—'sensitive', hidden reasons—why a child may be behaving badly. In doing so you may discover a source of anxiety in your child's life that you would never have considered possible.

ABUSE

If a child has been abused, whether physically, sexually or emotionally this will inevitably be reflected in his behaviour. You may think it beyond all possibility that your child could ever have been abused. You may say that you have never been violent with him, that you have always loved him, and that you could not even contemplate that he might have been sexually assaulted.

But the unfortunate fact is that physical, sexual and emotional abuse can occur without the perpetrators appreciating what they are doing. If the members of a family are in the habit of relating to one another in a highly aggressive manner, they may think that to verbally and physically harass a child is quite normal. Only when a serious physical assault takes place and is brought to the notice of the authorities do they become conscious of their inappropriate behaviour. Even sexual abuse can take place inadvertently: if adults are uninhibited in their sexual comments and habits and show no caution in exposing their child to explicit sex, they may unwittingly be abusing him; allowing a child to watch sex scenes on television could be regarded as a form of abuse.

Much abuse is, of course, deliberately perpetrated, but hidden from view. Sexual abuse, in particular, takes place in secret and the victim is extremely reluctant to reveal it.

So it is important to be aware of how abuse can take place, and of what might be the consequences.

Emotional abuse

Abuse can occur in any kind of family, rich or poor, but it usually takes place when the parents are preoccupied with their own concerns. It frequently occurs in young families where parents in their early twenties find it difficult to cope (see Violence in the Home, p. 41). In such families, where parents endure sustained material and relationship pressures, a child may be neglected. In addition to not being able to provide him with proper physical care and supervision, they may have neither the energy nor the enthusiasm to stimulate him through conversation and play. If he becomes the centre of their personal frustrations they may abuse him by threatening to leave, or by constantly criticising and rejecting him.

A young child who has been abused emotionally, who has not

formed a strong attachment to his parents—one in which he senses unconditional acceptance—will later be unable to relate well to other adults. He may reject *them* when they try to be friendly. Because of his insecurity, his confusion when trying to interpret their feelings, and his inability to express his own—other than through aggression—he may be constantly angry with other children. While he may have a very low self-esteem, some abused children think that they are well regarded, and in general terms rate themselves highly.

In this way the abuse he has suffered causes him to have a distorted view of the world.

Physical abuse

If a young child has been abused physically there is a great risk that he will later become aggressive and violent, that he will be antisocial and delinquent. This will depend on the degree of violence witnessed or experienced, his age when it happened, the relationship he had with the perpetrator and the amount of positive support he had around him, from either family or friends.

If an older child is abused he may withdraw into himself and become depressed. He may even contemplate suicide.

Child-abusing parents tend to have a very rigid view of what their child should be like and often think of him only in negative ways. They may regard him as being entirely stubborn or always irritable. Many such parents feel that they have no control over their lives, and that whatever happens is determined not by themselves but by fate. Their anxiety and frustration often prevent them, when their child poses a problem, from being a source of strength; instead, they physically abuse him.

Sexual abuse

If a child has been sexually abused, an emphasis on sex may come into his play and into his relationships with other children. He may make sexually inappropriate remarks, and initiate sexual contact with them or with adults. While the effect on some older children may be less marked because of their natural resilience and because they have a supportive network of friends—with one in particular in whom they are able to confide—in most cases sexual abuse has a devastating effect, both short- and long-term.

The child may have nightmares and be unable to sleep. He may experience flashbacks to the event and become generally very fearful. He may experience a loss of appetite or suffer severe and frequent stomach aches. He may start to wet the bed or soil himself. He may begin to self-injure by, for example, banging his head on the wall. Girls in particular may self-mutilate by lacerating their arms or burning their hands with cigarettes. They may become anorectic (p. 109). Boys may become extremely disobedient and antisocial. They may become aggressive and start to bully (p. 40). If they have been abused by a homosexual their problems may be compounded by a confused sense of their sexual identity.

Both boys and girls often experience a feeling of loss and isolation. They find it hard to place trust in anyone and have difficulty in relating to others, especially those of the opposite sex. While boys who have been abused by their fathers express their anger towards him, girls express anger to both the father and the mother. In these and other ways, older children are thought to be signalling their sense of guilt in not stopping the abuse and their sense of powerlessness in not being able to do so.

Abused children often develop very serious problems in later life: boys may turn out to be depressed adults with suicidal tendencies, and girls may be unable to experience sexual happiness. Their damaged potential for relating successfully to the opposite sex means that they often have short-term relationships, going from one unstable partnership to another.

Perhaps the most devastating effect of abuse on a child is that it may result in him becoming an abuser.

For all these reasons, it is important not only that parents and teachers examine whether a child may be suffering from abuse but that they do something to minimise the possibilities. If you are a parent of a child who is behaving badly, consider whether you might be venting your personal frustrations on him. Are you damaging him emotionally because you yourself feel abused? If you know that you have abused him, either physically or emotionally, or that you are on the verge of doing so, you should have no hesitation in seeking help (see Appendix A). Those who work with abused children appreciate the enormous stresses experienced by parents and are there to help them to cope with their feelings and to manage their children. They recognise, in particular, the enormous strain that a child with a disability or disorder can place on his family.

If you are a teacher you should, of course, be constantly alert to the fact that a child who has learning problems or who is behaving badly in school could be experiencing severe difficulties at home. You should be aware of the signs of abuse. For information on this—and what to do about it—refer to the guidance provided in your school's Child Protection Policy document.

BULLYING

Your child's behaviour may have deteriorated because he is being bullied.

Although schools have anti-bullying policies, the fact that much bullying is sustained and subtle, or occurs away from the view of teachers, means that many children continue to suffer in silence. While a great deal of bullying takes the form of verbal abuse, or emotional abuse by exclusion or ostracism, many boys and girls are subjected to a range of horrific physical experiences perpetrated by their peers. Working in gangs, bullies may give a child a severe beating—even break his bones or cause internal bleeding. These injuries may well be obvious, but if you question how they came about, even in these circumstances your child may be unwilling to tell you the truth. He may not wish to appear a wimp, or he may be afraid of the repercussions, should you take action.

It is, of course, most important to take action. If you do nothing he will continue to suffer, and he may be affected in later life.

Adults who were bullied as children report experiencing a range of severe difficulties. Women may be unable to trust anyone, may be afraid of new situations and have a fear of succeeding. Men have similar problems, but may also be uncommunicative and become loners. A high proportion of men and women who were bullied as children link the experience with their attempted or contemplated suicide.

And there is another possibility: although it may be hard for you to accept, your child may *be* a bully. There are many reasons why this may be so, but if you suspect that it is the case do seek immediate advice. A bully's future may be bleak: it is estimated that six out of ten boys who bully become criminals, convicted for aggressive and violent offences.

VIOLENCE IN THE HOME

Children are not only bullied at school—they can be bullied in the home. Again, as a parent you may be reluctant to consider this, and even feel insulted at the suggestion that this might be true in the case of your child. Similarly, if you are a professional you may have a very good impression of a given parent, and never suspect that her child could be at risk. But it is important that both parents and professionals do not deny possibilities.

Violence can take many forms. Even if a child is not physically abused himself he may, for instance, witness his parents being physically violent to one another or be continually exposed to their intense hostility. Because of their personal frustrations they may persistently scapegoat him, or place him under excessive pressure to achieve—often in aspects of their lives where they have failed. It is, of course, extremely important to acknowledge that severe physical abuse does take place. Child abuse is one of the commonest causes of death among pre-school children. Hundreds die each year as a result of maltreatment by their parents.

On the whole, we restrain our emotions in most social settings, but we usually feel able to unleash them within the confines of our homes. With some parents, this tendency takes an extreme form. They are reticent in public, thus maintaining their social respectability, while often violent at home. Those outside the family continue to acknowledge them as reasonable, self-controlled people with whom they can feel safe and on whom they can rely.

Thus it is that, unknown to others who may well feel quite close to a family, abuse can and does occur.

Abuse takes place across the whole social range, but as I mentioned above (see Emotional Abuse, p. 37) young parents in their twenties, in particular, are often unable to cope. This is a time when many have just begun to live independently, away from their own families. They may be in the first stages of learning to live with a new person, and beginning to find that they have committed themselves to an unrealistic partnership. A child may be a responsibility that they feel they cannot meet, either materially or emotionally. They may deeply resent the loss of their personal freedom; they may see their teenage dreams and aspirations disintegrating. They may perceive their personal situation to be unjust, and feel a sense of helplessness. They may feel that *they* are being abused. In addition, illness or unemployment may take them to breaking point, and in their frustration they may become aggressive, inflict violence on others, or withdraw from the world around them.

In circumstances like these, a child often becomes the target for aggression, especially if it is a child who demands a great deal of attention. Children who are sickly and continually cry often provoke abuse, particularly from parents who, because of their own fragility, are already under a great deal of stress. Parents who are violent towards their children know that they are doing something wrong, and their guilt aggravates the situation: they become increasingly frustrated and even more aggressive. They are ostracised by the community and their sense of isolation, which is often a trigger for the release of their uncontrolled emotions, is intensified. They feel that there is no one to turn to; they are incompetent, helpless and at the mercy of their emotions. They are abusers who feel abused.

Children also suffer at the hands of their brothers and sisters: 80 per cent of children between the ages of three and seventeen are involved in at least one annual incident of violent conflict with their siblings. One teenager in ten makes a violent attack annually on his parents, and 3 per cent of these attacks could be regarded as serious physical assault.

There may be no such level of violence in your home, but it is still worth considering how your child may be reacting to more subtle forms of aggression. And bear in mind, when doing so, that he may be particularly sensitive and unable to cope with stress. While most children benefit by being exposed to the vicissitudes of family life—in that they learn how to cope with feelings 'in the raw'—within an accepting environment, the more vulnerable child may react badly, especially if the family is failing to provide him with the extra amount of support that he needs.

CHANGE

We have already discussed how a child's behaviour may be affected by divorce (p. 29) or bereavement (p. 30). If her parents have divorced or if one of them has died, she will need to adjust to her new situation. She will have to begin forging new relationships within the home, and she may have difficulty in relating to a new parent. She may also be badly affected by the birth of a baby brother or sister: she may be faced with a change in her mother's attitude towards her—her mother may become less attentive and more negative or more controlling in her remarks to her. Or if an older brother or sister moves out of the home, the child may find it hard to cope with the separation. Another situation in which difficulties may crop up happens when, perhaps because of the need to pursue job opportunities, a family moves to a different location and the child has to enrol in another school. In many families this now occurs repeatedly, and while some children are able to adjust others are badly affected by the recurring loss of friends and regular routines. A child may also react badly if she moves class, or if her teacher leaves.

Common to all these events is the fact that the child's world changes.

It is important, therefore, when you are considering a change of any kind to bear in mind the effect that it may have on your child. If you know that she is particularly sensitive you should, for example, carefully balance the advantages of moving to a better job and a different location with *her* needs—and not presume that her interests necessarily coincide with yours.

If you are aware that your child has impending examinations, bear in mind the increased stress she may feel as a result of any changes in your circumstances that might occur just now. If you are her teacher, consider the effect that a change of class or even timetable may have on her. And consider also whether she can cope with the constant changing of location and teaching staff that may be required by your present curriculum arrangements.

While changes may be good for the majority of children—we all need to learn how to adapt—they can adversely affect the behaviour of those who are having to cope with personal problems. Above all else, such children need to develop a sense of personal security, and this cannot happen if their circumstances are continually altering.

THE WAY PARENTS BEHAVE

Relationships within the family have an even greater potential for inflicting lasting harm than do single events involving change. Although I have emphasised that a child's unwanted behaviour may be rooted within himself, he is heavily influenced by those who are close to him. Over a period of time, children copy the way their parents behave and adopt their pattern of relating to each other. They sense the way their parents feel and think and may act in a similar fashion. They observe their reaction to change and may build this into their own behaviour repertoire.

While modelling themselves on their parents can promote a positive self-image and a strong sense of identity, it will only do so if the parents have a good relationship in which they clearly care for each other and show mutual respect. If they never speak without quarrelling or becoming aggressive, or are unable to discuss matters or to cope with change themselves, this will be reflected in the learned behaviour of their children. And it will be more marked in a child who is vulnerable and who is more likely to be moulded by those around him.

The long-term effect of this process of 'learned' behaviour will be appreciated by those adults who are old enough to realise that they have gradually changed into their parent!

STYLES OF PARENTING

A child is also strongly influenced by the kind of discipline projected by his parents. If they impose rules too firmly and do not allow any negotiation, a child is likely to have a low self-esteem and may become withdrawn and miserable. The development of his conscience may be limited. If, by contrast, parents are over-indulgent and permissive, and there is no restriction on what their child is allowed to do, he will fail to develop controls over his impulses and may become aggressive. Faced with his constant demands, his parents may then become too harsh in an attempt to gain control—with equally adverse effects.

If a child has parents who are indifferent to what he does and do not involve themselves at all in his affairs, he may become aggressive, have little self-control, and low self-esteem.

It has been found that in the families of delinquent and aggressive children, parents

1 fail to provide their children with adequate supervision
2 fail to project clear and consistent rules and expectations
3 fail to show disapproval of behaviour such as stealing that they have not personally observed
4 avoid confrontation on important issues

5 are unable to react to crises other than emotionally
6 are unable to enforce rules because they have not developed meaningful relationships with their children by sharing enjoyable experiences with them.

When they are faced with a matter of discipline, these parents tend to do a lot of shouting but take little action. If they do take action it depends on their own mood at the time, rather than on the seriousness of what their child has done. Reacting on an emotional level, they reject their child rather than the specific behaviour of which they disapprove. They tend to criticise too much of what he does; consequently, whatever discipline they do try to impose is ignored.

Although it cannot be doubted that a difficult child himself plays a large part in promoting the style of parenting employed, because of his condition he is unable to do much about it. Parents, however, can make adjustments. The most effective style of parenting is thought to be one where the parents set firm, clear rules, and where the children are allowed to discuss and negotiate to a reasonable level. In this way the parents promote a sense of care, social responsibility, independence and self-esteem.

Although you may not recognise your parenting style from this brief summary, you may benefit by carefully assessing your approach to discipline and considering how it may or may not be adding to your child's problems. It is never too late to change, and there is nothing that cannot be improved. The same principles apply to teachers (see Relationships with Teachers, p. 49).

FAMILY SIZE

It is worth bearing in mind the potential effect of the size of your family on the behaviour of your difficult child. Although you cannot alter the situation you may, by making simple adjustments, be able to compensate for any adverse effects.

In general, children who come from larger families differ from those who live in small ones—in these respects. First, because there is less opportunity for parents to communicate with them they may have a lower level of verbal intelligence and reading attainment. They may not be encouraged so much to achieve academically. Second, large families often suffer from overcrowding and material hardship—in which parental discord and conflict are often rooted—and the level of control and the quality of discipline may be jeopardised. Children from large families may therefore be more restless, disobedient and destructive, or more liable to withdraw into themselves.

On the other hand, children from small families may suffer from the over-indulgence of their parents. An only child is often regarded as precious: he may have been born under difficult circumstances after a period of sterility, a series of miscarriages or the deaths of other children. It might be said that he is overvalued and overprotected. One of the parents may have excessive contact with him; she may mother him for too long, excluding all other relationships; she may prolong the process of infantile care, bathing and feeding, and generally be too much at his beck and call; she may prevent any move towards independence by not allowing him to help around the house and by trying to fight his battles for him. In many instances she will be emotionally dependent on him and, if she was raised in a home lacking warmth and love, she may be determined to give her child all the love she herself missed. If she has little or no social life with her partner, she may recognise the futility of her marital relationship and compensate by investing emotionally in her child.

If you have a large family, consider whether you spend an equal amount of time with each child or whether you have a favourite. Your difficult child's problems may be caused by the fact that he has little opportunity to express himself, or that he does not get enough of your attention. One thing you can do is make sure that each day you allocate a special time for him, and that you do something together. With a younger child you can read a story; an older child will benefit if you simply schedule a time in your mind when you ask him in general terms what he feels about a current news item, or if you explain your own problems to him. (We shall discuss the importance of effective communication on p. 132.)

If your family is small, ask yourself whether your life centres too much on your problem child and whether you are too protective. You could focus more on giving him his own space—allowing him time to play and to do what he wants, rather than organising things for him and feeling uneasy if he is not always achieving. More importantly, perhaps, you should think about cultivating your own interests. You need to become independent of your child and separate from him if he is to strengthen his own sense of identity.

If you are a teacher, remember that a child from a large family may need extra doses of affection and attention. In addition, you should also recognise the harmful effect of continually comparing him with his brothers and sisters, whom you may have taught.

Both the child from a large family and the child from a small one may need special help in developing a sense of identity and personal worth.

POSITION IN THE FAMILY

If you have a number of children, you will know that each is different in the way she thinks and behaves. To some extent, this may be linked to her position in the family. Generally, the first-born is likely to be a high achiever, both scholastically and at work, whereas the last born is more prone to scholastic failure.

The firstborn, though, is more likely to develop an emotional disorder. While she may receive more love and attention than her siblings, her parents may be more anxious, pressurising and controlling than they are with their subsequent children. As we noted above, she has also to adjust to the arrival of the others. She may regress in her toilet-training on the birth of a new baby. A hostile relationship often exists between siblings when there has been an intensely warm bond between the parent and the first child, while a rather more detached relationship between the parent and the firstborn can result in a more amicable interaction between the children.

Whether a child comes from a large or a small family, or whether she is the first or last born, does not necessarily indicate that she will present you with behavioural difficulties. The family is a phenomenon is which there is a great interplay of variables: the size of the family and the ordinal position of the child in it are just two of these.

It is important, all the same, to be aware of these aspects of family circumstances and of how the particularly difficult child may be affected. Again, although you cannot alter her position in the family you may be able to make simple and effective adjustments. You could, for example, help your firstborn by arranging to have a special time each day just for her (see Family Size, p. 46), or you could occasionally give new clothes, rather than hand-downs, to the others. Although these may appear to be small gestures, they can prevent a significant aggravation for more vulnerable children.

DIFFICULTIES AT SCHOOL (see Bullying, p. 40)

Early detection of problems

A child often only begins behaving badly when he starts school. On his own, at home, he may appear to have no problems. This is especially true if he is the firstborn and if his parents have little experience of how other children behave. While many have initial difficulties in coping with classmates, those who have underlying personal problems or learning disorders need early help if they are to avoid developing severe behavioural difficulties.

For example, a child may begin behaving badly if he has an inability to concentrate or if he suffers from hyperactivity. If his problem is not recognised and immediate adjustments made by the teacher, the situation will become worse. The child will compensate for his failure to keep up by behaving badly; or because he is hyperactive he will cause disruption. Over time he will be cast as the class nuisance and troublemaker—an identity which, through the inevitably intense negative attention given to him, will become deeply engrained.

In this way, a child who has an attention-deficit/hyperactivity disorder (see p. 59) may also come to suffer from a conduct disorder (see p. 62). On the other hand, a child with attention-deficit disorder (without hyperactivity), who is unable to do his work but who is quiet, dreamy and withdrawn, may be ignored and his underlying problem overlooked. He may become introspective and suffer from depression (see p. 112). It is therefore extremely important for both parents and teachers to be sensitive to a child's condition and to recognise the need to take early action.

If a child's difficulties are observed at an early age, simple adjustments at home and at school may prevent mild problems from developing into significant disorders.

Class size

If a child is behaving badly it may be that the size of his class is proving too much for him. He may not be able to get the help he needs with his learning, or he may be unable to tolerate the pressure of having so many others around him. While others may be able to cope—and indeed benefit from the large class setting in that they quickly learn how to relate to others—the problems of a child who has underlying difficulties may be exacerbated.

If he finds it hard to focus on his work, or is unable to control his impulses because of the level of distraction created by others, he will become increasingly disruptive. He will find it difficult to make friendships, and in his frustrated efforts to do so he will create enemies.

If he has to remain in a large class, it should be divided into subgroups: the aim here is to ensure that the self-esteem of all children is promoted. Provision should be made for those who have special needs to get the maximum amount of attention and supervision by the teacher, as well as opportunities to relate to others and the chance to regulate their own behaviour. But it may be that the particular child needs to be placed in a special setting. Both parents and teachers should always consider the value of this—and resist thinking that inclusive education is the only way forward. Although a child with a disorder may happily exist with those who have none, if his condition is severe it will be in his interest, and in the interest of the others in his class, if he is moved to a setting where he is not regarded as odd or as a troublemaker (see p. 123).

Relationships with teachers

When a child is experiencing difficulties with his work or with other children he will often focus on the shortcomings of his teacher. He may complain that she is picking on him. This will more often occur in a large class where resources are few and where the teacher may feel unable to make special arrangements for him. In her frustration she may indeed continually berate the child and make him feel victimised. She may bully and threaten him. In this way she may become embroiled in his interactional style, and thus promote it. The relationship between them may deteriorate to the point where each feels unable to tolerate the other.

Teachers have their own style, and this is reflected in the behaviour of the children they teach. If a teacher is loud, domineering and bullying, the children will tend to mirror this in their relationships with each other. The most sensitive children will become either more aggressive or more withdrawn. But if a teacher behaves with an effective blend of warmth and firmness, and regards himself more as a listening coach than a teacher, his children will be more understanding and helpful towards each other.

A complaint against a teacher could be an indication that the child himself is experiencing difficulties. This is often the case. Many children have problems in communicating their thoughts and feelings, and a child who has emotional problems may present a distorted view of his situation. He may, for example, complain about a teacher whom he really likes—what his complaints may really be signalling is his fear that she is about to leave. A complaining child may have learning difficulties that have remained undetected, and be unable to read; one who has difficulty in absorbing a particular subject may not be willing to admit this to himself, and may blame his problems on the subject teacher. A child who is ashamed of his lack of coordination or poor physique may say that he hates the PE teacher.

These, and a myriad other complaints, frequently crop up, and because of their potential for compounding behavioural problems they should not be ignored. A visit to the school to discuss the situation might result in a few simple adjustments being made—and a vast improvement in your child's behaviour.

CONCLUSION

In this chapter we have looked at further problems that might be contributing to your child's behaviour. Some may have raised issues in your mind that you prefer to ignore. But if you are to discover why he is behaving badly you must be prepared to consider even the most unlikely possibilities.

Don't be deterred from considering the sensitive subjects of abuse, bullying and violence. Regrettably, they are a fact of life that many deny, and because of the shame that they engender they are often hidden from view. Neither should you be afraid to examine the way in which you and your partner react to each other, and what kind of discipline you provide. Although your child will have had an enormous effect on the dynamics of your family, he is also heavily dependent on it. Because of his particular vulnerability, he is very susceptible to the influence of those around him. He will be relying on you to take the initiative and to question whether any adjustments need to be made either at home or at school.

* * *

In Part One we have examined the possibility of your child having a disorder and how this may have arisen. As I have stressed throughout, the process of assessing and diagnosing difficulties is extremely complex and must be left to experts. But by thinking carefully about the issues that we have covered you may now be in a better position to help your child.

You are probably reading this book because you have reached the stage where you desperately need help, either at home or in the classroom. What you have learned about the 'difficult' child and yourself in these first three chapters will be of great assistance if and when you refer to a specialist. On the other hand you may now feel that if you make a few adjustments, there may be no need to bother. You may feel that there are one or two things that you should do first, to see whether they will make the necessary difference.

Further help on how to deal with difficult children will be found in Part Three, where I have provided some basic principles of treatment for your consideration. To further enhance your appreciation of the difficulties that your child may be experiencing, in Part Two we shall look at some common childhood disorders.

Part Two

CHILDHOOD DISORDERS

You may feel that if you are able to more accurately define the nature of your child's difficulties you will be in a better position to do something about them. In essence, this is also the hope of specialists in childhood and adolescent problems, who are constantly striving to refine their diagnostic procedures. By continually assessing the effectiveness of their definitions, in terms of how successful they are in application, they are able to provide ever more effective treatment programmes.

In Part Two we shall look at some of the disorders that they have so far classified. First of all, it is important to realise that these descriptions of common problems are not absolute. They are an attempt to identify the causes of a child's behaviour, to predict outcomes and to establish the best course of treatment. Periodically, and according to a consensus of opinion on how far the classifications have proved successful, they are revised. Some categories are withdrawn or amended and others are added—in a continuous process of refinement.

As I have already mentioned, children invariably exhibit a wide range of co-morbid (coexisting) symptoms, and it is extremely difficult, if not impossible, to put their behaviour into a single category. So while it is necessary to define a problem as accurately as possible, to say that a child is suffering from a single specific disorder—as he might, for example, suffer from a specific physical illness such as epilepsy—may be attractive, but it could be misleading.

Many specialists would stress that it is far more useful in practical terms to think of treating a 'case' rather than a disorder. They would say this because each child brings to them a unique set of circumstances, the whole of which needs to be taken into account. If a consultant does describe your child as having a particular disorder, he may primarily be doing so for convenience: he may be emphasising how he sees your child's priorities in terms of treatment. This is not to say that disorders as such do not exist. While greater definition is still needed, the process of refinement has indicated that there are certain conditions that have their own distinctive characteristics.

The important thing, however, is to focus on finding a solution to your child's problems; classifying his behaviour should be regarded only as a means to this end.

* * *

In considering, next, the characteristics of some of the disorders so far classified, my purpose is to inform you of possibilities. From what I have already said, it will be clear that it would be extremely unwise to jump to conclusions about the behaviour of your child. We all have a tendency towards hypochondria—to imagine that we have the very illness that we have just read about. So beware of seizing on what you read and instantly applying it to your child—or to yourself. The characteristics listed in the descriptions in this book are found in most human beings. It is only when they are *severe, persistent and socially disabling* that they may be regarded as significant—and only a highly trained specialist such as a paediatrician, a clinical psychologist or a psychiatrist can make this decision.

His assessment will be comprehensive and complex. He will consider your child's problems in relation to a wide range of possible clinical and personality disorders. He will examine her general medical condition, and he will attempt to discover whether she has been affected by anything that may have occurred at home, at school or in the neighbourhood. Your child's school will be consulted, and other specialists such as educational psychologists will be involved in the assessment. Only when the interaction of all these facets has been considered in relation to how she is generally coping will a reasonable diagnosis be possible. (Be wary of a specialist who gives you an instant diagnosis—*and* cure!)

When you have considered all the issues raised elsewhere in this book you will be well prepared to play your part in reaching some useful conclusions—not only about the possibility of your child suffering from a disorder but, more importantly, about what *you* might do to help her.

* * *

The order in which the following disorders are presented has no particular significance, and the broad 'problem' groupings are indicated only for your convenience. Descriptions of specific disorders are presented in a generalised way, and because of the limitations of this book they are by no means comprehensive.

The 'official' diagnostic criteria for some disorders (asterisked in the text) are reprinted in Appendix B. It is worth noting that, while a child must meet all the criteria if a firm diagnosis is to be made, her condition may be assessed as 'mild', 'moderate' or 'severe', depending on the number of symptoms in excess of the basic requirements and the degree to which her performance is being impaired.

It is also worth noting that a child who does not meet the full criteria for a disorder, but displays some of the characteristics, may still have a serious and significant condition. So don't be deterred from seeking further advice because your child does not seem to fit neatly into any of the following classifications.

4 Disorders relating to Hyperactivity/ Attention Deficits, Antisocial Behaviour and Substance Use

We shall begin in this chapter with a broad group of children who are probably the most disruptive in the classroom and the most disagreeable in the home and in the community. On the surface they are healthy youngsters with no apparent disability—and because of this they appear to be extremely naughty when they are young and deliberately obnoxious and defiant when older. The fact that on occasions they can be a pleasure to be with only adds fuel to the fire. Their behaviour exasperates and exhausts all those who come into contact with them. As they are commonly regarded as children who can behave well if they want to, it is often felt that all they have lacked is a 'good hiding'.

They include the quiet and the dreamy, the frustratingly withdrawn, the lethargic and the apathetic—but also those extremely active children whose boundless energy drives everyone to distraction. Also in this group I place those who may be so persistently antisocial and unafraid of authority that their behaviour is often felt to reflect some innate evilness. These children seem unable to conform or to appreciate the consequences of their actions. They appear impervious to the feelings of others. These are the 'hard men'—the thugs of the classroom and the terrors of the neighbourhood. They can be openly defiant, extremely hostile and aggressive. Some of them are into the drug culture and on the periphery of crime.

I have grouped together the disorders from which these kinds of children may be suffering because they are all thought to be interlinked: if a child is suffering from attention-deficit/hyperactivity disorder and this goes undetected, he may be rejected by his classmates, develop antisocial behaviour and become excessively defiant (oppositional defiant disorder). If, in turn, this problem is not addressed he may become more specifically antisocial and be regarded as having conduct disorder.

PROBLEMS TO DO WITH STAYING STILL AND ON TASK

Attention-deficit/hyperactivity disorder*

1 What is it?

A child with this disorder will show symptoms of inattention *and/or* hyperactivity/impulsivity:

- *Inattention* He may often appear not to be listening to what he is told, and may seem unable to sustain his interest in an activity or conversation. He may flit from one thing to another and only stay on task when the activity is highly stimulating and providing him with immediate feedback—otherwise, he will be easily distracted and will fail to complete tasks or to follow instructions. He may be extremely disorganised, pay little attention to detail and make many careless mistakes.
- *Hyperactivity* The child will appear to have boundless energy. He will find it difficult to play quietly or to remain seated for any length of time. He will never stop fidgeting, will talk excessively and loudly, and will appear permanently restless.
- *Impulsivity* He will speak or act on impulse and without thinking of the consequences, even when these may be potentially dangerous. He will intrude on others by interrupting conversations, making inappropriate comments or by generally having difficulty in turn-taking.

There are three AD/HD subtypes:

(i) *Combined* The child displays symptoms of both inattention and hyperactivity/impulsivity.
(ii) *Predominantly inattentive* He displays more symptoms of inattention than of hyperactivity/impulsivity.
(iii) *Predominantly hyperactive/impulsive* He displays more symptoms of hyperactivity/impulsivity than of inattention.

2 *Is it a very common disorder?*
It is estimated by some to occur in 3–5 per cent of schoolchildren; others put the figure as high as 19 per cent.

3 *At what age does it appear?*
The disorder is difficult to detect below the age of four or five because such young children generally display many of its characteristics and are rarely required to stay on task. However, even before this age a child may, for example, be unable to sit still for long enough to have a meal or listen to a story, and be described as generally unmanageable. Problems are commonly highlighted when he starts school and is unable either to succeed in his work because of his inattentiveness or to conform to classroom rules because of his hyperactivity/impulsivity.

4 *Can both boys and girls have it?*
Although it is more common in boys, it is also observed in girls.

5 *Is it inherited?*
It is thought to be inherited. Many children with the disorder have fathers who also had it when they were children; a smaller number have mothers who in their childhood may have been described as having it. Family members of a child with this disorder are also more likely than others to suffer from mood and anxiety disorders, learning disorders, substance-related disorders or antisocial personality disorders.

6 *Does the child get better?*
With time, problems may diminish for some sufferers, but in other cases the adverse effects of the disorder may increase during the stressful period of adolescence, leading to either complex school-related problems or antisocial and criminal behaviour. For some, severe problems continue to be experienced into adulthood. Prospects for children who are predominantly inattentive are considerably better than for those who are predominantly hyperactive/impulsive. The latter are at great risk of developing conduct disorder (p. 62).

In general there is a fair chance that a child will eventually get better, but a great deal will depend on the level of his hyperactivity and aggression, on whether or not he also exhibits the symptoms of conduct disorder, on his intelligence, on family influences and on how much support he receives from both home and school.

7 *Could he have another disorder at the same time as this one?*
A child with this disorder will almost inevitably display the symptoms of other disorders. It is estimated that approximately 70 per cent of children with this disorder have coexisting (co-morbid) conditions. Many have oppositional defiant disorder (Appendix B and p. 65) or conduct disorder. They may also suffer from other conditions such as mood disorders, anxiety disorders (see Chapter 6), communication or learning disorders (see Chapter 5) or Tourette's disorder (p. 106).

8 *Could the behaviour be caused by something other than AD/HD?*
The behaviour of a child with this disorder may also be observed in others, but it would not necessarily mean that they had AD/HD:

- A child who has a low level of mental ability will often display symptoms of inattention, or hyperactivity/impulsivity—especially if, for example, his school setting is inappropriate.
- A child who is highly intelligent may do likewise.
- A child who comes from a chaotic background may know no other form of behaviour: he may appear unable to stay on task, be disorganised and act in a highly impulsive manner only because those around him do so.
- A child who persistently refuses to perform tasks that require sustained effort may be displaying *oppositional* behaviour rather than symptoms of AD/HD—that is, behaviour that could be explained as a reluctance to do anything that requires sustained, focused attention.
- A child displaying some of the characteristics of AD/HD may be suffering from another disorder such as one of those mentioned in point 7 above.

9 *What will be the effect of the disorder on the child?*

- He may be underachieving academically, and attach little importance to success.
- He may have low self-esteem, and more enemies than friends.

- He may be prone to accidents.

10 How am I likely to feel about a child with this disorder?
You may be irritated because he cannot concentrate on anything for more than a few minutes at a time: he may appear to be completely disorganised and incapable of completing any task that you set him. You may feel exhausted because he is constantly restless and 'on the go'. Because he is so impulsive and unpredictable you may be constantly on edge.

Occasionally a child with this condition gets things right and is a pleasure to be with: this may make you feel that for the rest of the time he is simply lazy, or deliberately being naughty.

ANTISOCIAL BEHAVIOUR AND DISOBEDIENCE

(a) Conduct disorder*

1 What is it?
A child with this disorder will display antisocial behaviour. He may be aggressive to people and animals, destroy property, steal and be deceitful and break rules:

- *Aggression to people and animals* The child may bully and intimidate others. He may get involved in fights and use weapons that can cause serious harm. He may be cruel to animals and terrorise them.
- *Destruction of property* He may deliberately destroy or vandalise the property of others; he may smear buildings with graffiti or set fire to them.
- *Deceitfulness and theft* He may be involved in theft, or breaking and entering. He may have to lie to obtain what he wants.

There are two subtypes:

(i) *Childhood-onset type* The child displays at least one of the characteristics of the disorder before he is ten years old.
(ii) *Adolescent-onset type* He does not display any of the characteristics of the disorder before he is ten years old.

In the mild form of the disorder the child's behaviour will cause little harm to others; in severe cases he will be involved in a wide range of antisocial behaviours, which will cause considerable harm.

2 *Is it a very common disorder?*
This is the most common disorder. It is estimated by some that it occurs in 4 per cent of children who live in the country and in 9 per cent of those who live in towns and cities. Others claim that in certain groups of children it is as high as 16 per cent.

3 *At what age does it occur?*
The disorder can occur in children as young as five, but more commonly appears in late childhood or early adolescence. It is rare for it to begin after the age of sixteen. In most cases the symptoms change with age and with the physical development of the child: less serious behaviours such as shoplifting and fighting may be observed when the child is young; symptoms displayed by teenagers may include assault, burglary and rape.

4 *Can both girls and boys have it?*
Although it is more common in boys—the childhood-onset type is much more common in boys—it is also observed in girls. Boys with the disorder are generally more aggressive than the girls. While they are commonly involved in fighting, stealing, vandalism and discipline problems, girls are more likely to lie, to truant and to run away, and to be involved in substance abuse or prostitution.

5 *Is it inherited?*
It is thought that the disorder is both inherited *and* created by the circumstances in which the child finds himself. He is more likely to have it if a parent has one of a number of disorders such as personality disorder, a mood disorder, schizophrenia or attention-deficit disorder.

6 *Does the child get better?*
The prospects for a child with the disorder are variable. If he has it before the age of ten he will fare much worse than if he doesn't display its characteristics until adolescence—he is more likely, with early onset, to develop antisocial personality disorder, mood disorder or anxiety disorders in adulthood or to become involved in substance abuse. Most adults who have had conduct disorder

in childhood continue to have social problems. However, in some cases the child makes the necessary adjustments as he grows older and the symptoms disappear.

7 *Could he have another disorder at the same time as this one?*
Many children who have this disorder also have attention-deficit/hyperactivity disorder. They also commonly have learning disorders, communication disorders, anxiety disorders, mood disorders and substance-related disorders.

8 *Could the behaviour be caused by something other than conduct disorder?*
Some of the behaviour of a child with this disorder may also be observed in others, but it would not necessarily mean that they had conduct disorder:

- A disruptive child whose behaviour appears to be antisocial may be suffering from hyperactivity/impulsivity.
- A child who is antisocial may be of low intelligence.
- A child who is unable to conform may be predominantly defiant and oppositional, or have problems related to communication.
- A child who does not 'fit in' may be suffering from anxiety or have a mood disorder.
- A child may be reacting to circumstances around him or reflecting the setting in which he exists: by acting in an antisocial way he may, in a sense, be conforming.
- A child displaying some of the characteristics of conduct disorder may be suffering from another disorder such as one of those mentioned in point 7 above.

9 *What will be the effect of the disorder on the child?*

- He may appear to have little concern for others.
- He may have a hostile view of the world.
- He may appear to have no feelings of remorse.
- He may appear tough, but have low self-esteem.
- He may appear volatile, reckless and prone to accidents.
- He may smoke, drink and indulge in sexual behaviour at an early age. He may be involved in drug-taking.
- His level of achievement in school will be low.
- He will be disliked.

- Because of his behaviour he may be excluded from school or involved with the law.
- He may attempt suicide.

10 How am I likely to feel about a child with this disorder?
You may be extremely concerned about his future. You may feel that he has been involved in so many antisocial acts that he will inevitably end up behind bars. You may feel deeply worried because of his apparent need to hurt people, or be disturbed by the cruel way he treats animals. The fact that he appears never to learn from his mistakes or to express genuine remorse makes you extremely apprehensive when you consider his prospects.

(b) Oppositional defiant disorder*
1 What is it?
A child with this disorder will be negative, defiant, disobedient and hostile to authority figures. He will frequently:

- lose his temper
- argue with adults
- actively defy adults or refuse to comply with their requests or rules
- deliberately do things that will annoy others
- blame others for his behaviour
- be easily annoyed by others
- be angry and resentful
- be spiteful or vindictive.

2 Is it a very common disorder?
It is estimated that it occurs in 2–16 per cent of children.

3 *At what age does it occur?*
The characteristic behaviours are usually observed before the child is eight years old, and not later than early adolescence.

4 *Can both girls and boys have it?*
Both boys and girls may have the disorder. Before puberty it is more prevalent in boys, but teenage boys and girls suffer from it equally. Boys tend to be more openly confrontational than girls and their symptoms are more persistent.

5 *Is it inherited?*
The disorder is more common in children who come from families where one of the parents has had a disorder of his or her own, such as mood disorder, attention-deficit disorder, conduct disorder, personality disorder. The mother of a child with the disorder is more likely to suffer from depression, but whether this is the result or cause of her child's disorder is unclear.

6 *Does the child get better?*
The disorder often precedes the development of conduct disorder (p. 62).

7 *Could he have another disorder at the same time as this one?*
Many children with this disorder have attention-deficit/hyperactivity disorder (p. 59). They may also have learning and communication disorders (see Chapter 5).

8 *Could his behaviour be caused by something other than oppositional defiant disorder?*
Some of the behaviour of a child with this disorder may also be observed in others, but this would not necessarily mean that they had oppositional defiant disorder:

- A child who refuses to do what he is told may be predominantly inattentive.
- A child who is defiant and disobedient, or spiteful, may be predominantly antisocial.
- His defiance may be symptomatic of a mood disorder.
- The child may be reacting to the circumstances in which he finds himself.
- He may be suffering from one of the disorders mentioned in point 7 above.

9 *What will be the effect of the disorder on the child?*

- He may appear stubborn.
- He may be unwilling to compromise or negotiate.
- He may constantly test boundaries and limits.
- He may be irritating and annoying.
- He may be verbally (rather than physically) hostile and aggressive.

- He may not accept that there is anything wrong with his behaviour, and blame everyone else.
- He may be intolerant of others and in conflict with parents, teachers and friends.
- He may use foul language, smoke, drink or take drugs.
- He will have low self-esteem.

10 How am I likely to feel about a child with this disorder?
You may feel, with shame, that you have become as stubborn as your child and that you are both 'at battle stations'. You may be worried about what you may do to him if his defiance persists. You may be concerned for his future and feel that he will inevitably end up in serious trouble.

PROBLEMS TO DO WITH ALCOHOL, TOBACCO, SOLVENTS AND DRUGS

Substance-related disorder

1 What is it?
A child with this disorder will continue to take a substance despite being aware that it is doing him harm. There is a wide range of these disorders. Each is associated with a particular substance and has its own symptoms and characteristics. For example, there are alcohol-related disorders, amphetamine-related disorders, nicotine-related disorders, and many others.

A child who has the disorder will usually display one or more of the following symptoms, which are characteristic of most of the subtypes:

(i) *Substance dependence* A child who is dependent on a substance will continue to use it despite the clear problems that it is causing him. He may display the following symptoms:

- compulsive use (the principal characteristic of the disorder) Although he may express a desire and a firm intention to stop taking the substance, he will continue to do so. It may assume a central position in his life—everything may revolve around it. He will spend most of his time either acquiring the substance, using it or recovering from its effects. He will prefer to take it rather than spend time socialising or participating in other activities.

- tolerance He will need ever-increasing amounts of the substance to achieve the desired effect. Much will depend on the substance being taken: there is a greater chance of a child becoming more tolerant—that is, needing more—of amphetamines than of alcohol, but the need for alcohol can also assume great significance. He may also become tolerant of nicotine or cannabis. Often he will be unaware of how his body may have adjusted in this way and not realise how dependent he has become.
- withdrawal The child will suffer specific unpleasant effects associated with the 'wearing off' of a particular substance—and will take more (rather than less) of it to avoid the sensation. He may crave the substance, to alleviate the unpleasantness experienced when his intake is either stopped or reduced.

(ii) *Substance abuse* Because of repeatedly taking the substance he will experience harmful social and interpersonal problems. He will fail to fulfil his obligations, and may place himself or others at risk. For example, he may truant from school or he may fail to produce his work; he may be under the influence of the substance when he is placed in a position of responsibility at home. Despite the substance creating all sorts of problems with other people and devastating his social life, he still persists in using it.
(iii) *Substance intoxication* The child's central nervous system will be affected by his taking the substance. During or shortly after taking it his mood may change; he may be unable to think properly or do things that he would normally find easy. The degree and the way in which he will be adversely affected will depend on the substance taken, the amount, how tolerant he is, and the social setting. The effect of intoxication may last for a long time: even after the substance has been eliminated from the body, the symptoms may persist. If the intake substance is reduced, the symptoms may disappear. The child may, however, suffer from withdrawal (see above).

2 Is it a very common disorder?
A large number of children experiment with a variety of substances, but since most surveys only ask whether a child has ever used a substance, it is difficult to estimate how many have a significant substance-related disorder. The number is thought to

be low. The most commonly taken substances are those that are most socially acceptable—alcohol, tobacco and marijuana (cannabis). But children also experiment with solvents, other illegal drugs and tranquillisers.

It is estimated that 3–5 per cent of children aged eleven to sixteen have used cannabis, and that this number rises in teenagers to 17 per cent. There has also been a dramatic increase in the number of children who have taken hallucinogens such as Ecstasy or LSD. The number using heroin or cocaine is much lower, but in certain areas it is thought to be on the increase. The availability of substances and our confused and ambiguous attitude to them will probably lead to the disorder increasing among our children.

3 *At what age does it appear?*

A great deal depends on the substance being taken. While pre-teen children may take tobacco or inhale solvents, other substances such as cannabis or Ecstasy are more commonly misused in the teenage years. In general, substance-related disorder most often appears during adolescence and beyond.

4 *Can both boys and girls have it?*

Both may misuse substances: ratios vary according to age, location and the substance being misused.

5 *Is it inherited?*

It is unclear whether in general terms substance-related disorder is inherited. It is thought that a child may be more predisposed to it if other family members have antisocial problems of their own. However, studies focusing on alcohol-related disorders, which have been more extensive, do indicate that these in particular may in some way be inherited.

6 *Does the child get better?*

The prospects for a child with the disorder vary according to his emotional, intellectual and physical makeup, the nature of the substance being taken and the severity of his condition. With treatment the symptoms may be considerably alleviated; in some cases they may disappear. However, in general, severe substance-related disorders persist in one form or another for many years, with only brief periods of remission.

The problem is made worse by other disorders such as depression (see p. 112), which tend to coexist or develop alongside the disorder.

7 *Could he have another disorder at the same time as this one?*
There is a strong possibility that a child with a substance-related disorder will also have conduct disorder or a mood disorder.

8 *Could the behaviour be caused by something other than substance-related disorder?*
Some of the behaviour of a child with this disorder may also be observed in others, but this would not necessarily mean that they had substance-related disorder:

- A child whose speech is slurred and who generally gives the impression of being intoxicated may be suffering from a medical condition or have a head injury.
- A child who is uninterested in everything, who fails to do his schoolwork, may be suffering from anxiety or have attention-deficit disorder.
- A child who appears withdrawn and 'unreachable' may be suffering from depression.
- A child who is aggressive and involved in antisocial acts may be suffering from conduct disorder.
- A child may have one of a number of other conditions that is being aggravated by the substance he is taking. For example, if he becomes severely anxious on taking a substance, he may already have an anxiety disorder; if he becomes extremely 'low', he may be suffering from depression. The substance exaggerates the condition.

9 *What will be the effect of the disorder on the child?*
He will display a number of symptoms specifically associated with the substance that he has taken (it is beyond the scope of this book to describe these). In general:

- He may have a deficient diet because he prefers the substance to food.
- He may not bother with his personal hygiene.
- He may become physically ill.

- He may become aggressive or withdrawn.
- He may have suicidal tendencies.
- Taking the substance may induce other disorders: for instance, either when he is intoxicated or when he is suffering from withdrawal he may have difficulty sleeping, or he may become grossly anxious or psychotic.
- Because of his antisocial behaviour he will have few friends; those he does have will have antisocial tendencies themselves.
- Although he may appear not to care about the world around him and to have a high opinion of his worth, he will have low self-esteem and will relate to others in a very defensive manner.

10 How am I likely to feel about a child with this disorder?
If your child has simply been experimenting with substances you may be unconcerned: the majority of young people will also have done this. However, if your child shows significant symptoms you may be extremely worried at the risk he is taking with his health. You may also be concerned at the company he is keeping and the fact that he is sacrificing so many good friends and opportunities for something that might ultimately kill him.

You may be bewildered by the fact that although your child is reasonably intelligent he is unable to respond to logic: he knows that he should give up, but he cannot do so. He appears to be compelled to continue using the substance. You know that his habit will have severe repercussions on his health, and fear that it may lead him into a life of crime.

CONCLUSION

If you have been able to recognise your child from these descriptions—and even though you may have concluded that he could indeed have one or more of the disorders—you may, curiously, have experienced a sense of relief. I hope that this is because you now feel that there is a glimmer of hope for the future and that things can begin to move forward. Whereas before you were one of those who regarded your child as deliberately and consciously obnoxious, and could only either condemn him or try to beat sense into him, you are now able to think of him more positively.

If you *are* feeling this way, perhaps you have begun to detach yourself from your child—to be less emotional about his behaviour; perhaps you are starting to understand that he may have a condition that can be treated.

If, on the other hand, you have become even more concerned by reading of the disorders, don't despair. Although many of them cannot be completely cured, a great deal can be done to help your child. Recognising that he may have a disorder is the first step towards doing something about it. Referral to a specialist who will make a more accurate assessment of his difficulties is the next step to take. Her diagnosis will form the basis of a treatment programme that could ultimately—and quickly, in some cases—lead to a transformation in your child's behaviour.

5 Disorders concerned with Relating and Communicating, Learning and Coordination

Perhaps the most disheartening situation for a parent or teacher is to feel that he is unable to 'connect' with the 'difficult' child—when he receives no feedback from her.

In this chapter we shall look briefly at some disorders that describe children who are hard to reach and who may present very difficult management problems. Among these children are those who appear to be locked in their own world and to prefer objects to people—they have no apparent desire to link up with others, to share and to have a relationship; and then there are those who want to make friendships but because of their condition are unable to do so. In their frustration such children may exhibit bizarre behaviour; they may be unable to tolerate change and may rely heavily on routines and schedules; they may have unusual and obsessional interests.

We shall also look at those who have particular difficulty in expressing themselves and at others who not only find it hard to do so but are unable to understand what is being said to them. Although they have normal intelligence, their ability to either receive messages from others or to express themselves is not as it should be. We shall also hear of children who are quite capable of speaking but who fail to speak in certain social situations.

We shall briefly describe dyslexia, a learning disorder from which many children (and adults) suffer, and which often occurs in children who present a variety of severe behavioural problems.

You may have had some contact with a child who has one of these disorders, or know of special facilities in your area that cater for such children; you may be aware of their difficulties and of the severe problems that they present for their parents and their teachers. If this is the case, you may feel that your child could not possibly be a sufferer—that if, for example, she had autistic disorder you would certainly already know about it. But it is worth reminding yourself that the children who attend special facilities will most likely have been diagnosed as meeting the full criteria for the disorder, whereas others may exhibit less severe symptoms.

Difficulties in communicating and relating to others vary wildly, and they interrelate in a highly complex way that is not fully understood even by experts. Do bear in mind, as I said earlier, that the characteristics of certain children have been grouped together in 'disorders' only for the purpose of providing effective treatment for the individual child. It is important to realise this and to recognise that, for example, a child who may not suffer from autistic disorder could be described as having both some autistic features and some characteristics of mixed receptive-expressive language disorder (see p 82); he may be described as being 'in the autistic spectrum'—that is, having some of the characteristics of autistic disorder.

Remember that in this section of the book we are taking a brief look at the following disorders only for the purpose of being more specific about your child's behaviour. Even though you may feel that she could not possibly be suffering, for instance, from autistic disorder, learning about its characteristics may help you to better analyse her difficulties and to focus on specific problems when you are trying to cope with her.

PROBLEMS WITH RELATING TO OTHERS, COMMUNICATING, AND UNUSUAL BEHAVIOUR OR INTERESTS

(a) Autistic disorder*

1 What is it?

A child with this disorder will display difficulties in relating to and communicating with others, and will have a restricted, repetitive repertoire of activities and interests.

- *Relating to others* His ability to communicate non-verbally will be impaired. In his interactions with others, his eye-to-eye contact and facial expressions will be unusual. He will not use appropriate body postures and gestures.

While the younger child may have no interest in making friends, the older child may wish to do so but be unsuccessful because of his lack of appreciation of social conventions. He will not spontaneously seek to share his enthusiasms or interests, and will prefer to indulge in solitary activities. If he does involve others, it will be because they are essential to his purpose.

He will be unable to interpret the behaviour of others or to understand what they are thinking. They will find it difficult to 'connect' with his feelings, and he is unlikely to inquire about theirs. He may appear to be more involved with objects, or parts of them, which appear to others to have no particular attraction.

- *Communicating* The child may not begin to speak as early as he should, nor communicate otherwise by, for example, using gestures. When he *can* speak he will find it hard to start and/or sustain a conversation, and may speak in a monotone or with inappropriate emphasis. He may repeat phrases that he has heard from somewhere but that are meaningless in their present context. He may be unable to understand simple jokes, to be on the same wavelength as the other person.

  In his play the young child will show a lack of spontaneity or creativity; he may not indulge in make-believe or role play. He will not smile spontaneously at people or respond to their smiles, and will rarely ask what another person is thinking or feeling.
- *Restricted, repetitive behaviour and interests* The child may have a preoccupation with one particular interest and accrue an enormous store of information on it. He may, for example, know precise details of complicated railway timetables or memorise vast banks of sporting data.

  He may adhere to fixed routines and rituals and react badly to any kind of change. Small alterations to his room may upset him, and if the daily pattern of events is changed he may be unable to cope. In his play he may repeat the same action over and over again and be fascinated with anything that moves; he may be strongly attached to a seemingly insignificant object such as a shoe-lace, a piece of paper or a bottle top. He may repeatedly walk in an unusual way—for instance, tip-toe; he may flap or clap his hands, or sit rocking his body.

2 *Is it a very common disorder?*
Autism is very rare. It is estimated that it occurs in 2–5 children out of every ten thousand.

3 *At what age does it appear?*
The disorder occurs before the age of three, but the symptoms are often hard to detect—they are more easily observed between the ages of four and six.

4 *Can both boys and girls have it?*
Although both can have it, boys suffer most, with 4–5 times as many having the condition.

5 *Is it inherited?*
It is thought that it is inherited: a child is more likely to have the disorder if one of his parents has it.

6 *Does the child get better?*
Improvements may be seen in some cases, and usually occur during the early teens when his behaviour may become more flexible. But during adolescence there is the possibility that he may become more aggressive and more difficult to manage. A great deal depends on the severity of the condition, on the child's level of intelligence and on his ability to communicate. While some go on to make improvements into their late twenties and early thirties, the condition never dissipates completely: even an intelligent child with the disorder will continue to have difficulties in relating to others in adulthood. Although he may achieve a greater degree of independence, he will still require a strong network of support.

7 *Could he have another disorder at the same time as this one?*
A child with this disorder is highly likely also to have a mental disability and a communication disorder (see p. 80).

8 *Could the behaviour be caused by something other than autism?*
Some of the behaviour of a child with this disorder may also be observed in others, but it would not necessarily mean that they had autism:

- A child who appears to be unresponsive when spoken to may have difficulties with his hearing.
- A child who has difficulty in communicating may be suffering from a specific language disorder which prevents him from receiving messages or expressing himself (see p. 80).
- A child who appears to have unusual body movements may have coordination problems (see p. 89).
- A child who seems unable to communicate, who appears detached or who displays bizarre or repetitive behaviour, may be excessively anxious (see p. 94).
- A child whose language development is delayed, or whose behaviour may seem unusual or repetitive, may have suffered serious physical, intellectual or emotional neglect.
- A child who has no significant language delay and is of normal intelligence may be displaying the symptoms of Asperger's disorder (see Appendix B and p. 78).
- A child who is unable to understand others or express himself may have a mental disability or a communication disorder.

9 *What will be the effect of the disorder on the child?*

- He may appear unreachable and unlovable.
- He may not appear to connect with others—to be on the same wavelength.
- He may be aggressive, hyperactive and impulsive. He may be inattentive.
- He may be unpredictable: he may become distressed for no apparent reason or appear to have no sense of danger.
- His behaviour may appear bizarre: he may injure himself by biting his wrist or banging his head against the wall.
- In pursuing his obsession with one, seemingly meaningless, interest he will appear totally self-centred—an eccentric loner.
- He will have no friends, and as he becomes older and more aware of his condition he may also become depressed.

10 How am I likely to feel about a child with this disorder?
You may feel that he is locked in his own world and that you cannot reach him. The fact that he seems to relate to objects more than to people may make you feel that he simply does not need you. His inability to spontaneously connect with a smile, or to express surprise and delight, may reinforce your sense of isolation from him.

This, together with his need to adhere to rigid schedules and routines, may frustrate and depress you. The fact that he never initiates any meaningful interaction may make your efforts seem pointless.

(b) Asperger's disorder*

1 What is it?

A child with this condition will display some of the characteristics of autistic disorder (see Appendix B and p. 74): he will have difficulty in interacting and communicating with others, and will have a restricted, repetitive repertoire of activities and interests. The disorder differs in presentation from autism in that:

- A child with Asperger's disorder will not experience difficulties in language development, nor will he suffer from mental disability.
- The symptoms are not so severe: his behaviour will be less bizarre and his interests will not be so restricted as those of a child with autism.
- A child with Asperger's disorder may appear to like social contact and try hard to be sociable.
- He may appear to suffer from clumsiness.

2 *Is it a very common disorder?*

It is estimated that it occurs in a minimum of 3–7 people in every ten thousand.

3 *At what age does it appear?*

The symptoms are usually highlighted in the first years of schooling, when the child's behaviour and interactions with others are observed. However, the disorder may go undetected until later, and even until adulthood. A great deal depends on the severity of the child's condition and on whether any associated behaviours cause significant disruption either at home or at school.

4 *Can both boys and girls have it?*

The disorder occurs in both, but boys are four times more likely to be sufferers.

5 *Is it inherited?*

It occurs more frequently in the children of those who are sufferers themselves.

6 *Does the child get better?*
As he becomes older he may learn to adapt to his condition, but the symptoms will not disappear completely. In adulthood, a sufferer may continue to have difficulty in understanding and empathising with others, in planning his life and in coping with change.

7 *Could he have another disorder at the same time as this one?*
A child with this disorder could also suffer from attention-deficit/hyperactivity disorder, or depression, in adolescence.

8 *Could the behaviour be caused by something other than Asperger's disorder?*
Some of the behaviour of a child with this disorder may also be observed in others, but it would not necessarily mean that they had Asperger's disorder:

- A child who appears to be unresponsive when spoken to may have difficulties with his hearing.
- One who appears to have unusual (or clumsy) body movements may have coordination problems (see Dyspraxia, p. 89).
- One who displays bizarre behaviour may be suffering from an anxiety disorder.
- A child whose behaviour is unusual or repetitive may have suffered serious physical, intellectual or emotional neglect.
- One who appears inattentive or impulsive/hyperactive and who is unable to organise his life may be suffering from attention-deficit/hyperactivity disorder (see p. 59).
- A child who appears detached, solitary and unhappy may be suffering from depression (see p. 112).

9 *What will be the effect of the disorder on the child?*

- He may seem to want to connect with others—to have friends—but be unable to do so because of his inability to empathise with their thoughts and feelings.
- His words and actions may appear to be naïve and he may display socially inappropriate behaviour. He may therefore be regarded as odd, even eccentric, by his peers.
- Although he may excel at learning facts and figures he may find it hard to think in an abstract way.

- Despite his average or above-average intelligence he may appear to have little 'common sense'. He may seem solitary and unhappy as he becomes more aware of his difficulties.

10 How am I likely to feel about a child with this disorder?
You may feel that he is intelligent and that there are occasions when he seems able to communicate and relate well to people. Your frustration at his constant relapses into inappropriate, socially naïve behaviour, or his inability to get to grips with his life, is therefore intensified.

You may be constantly aware of his inability to 'connect' and saddened at the loneliness that you feel he too must be experiencing. You may feel that if only he knew how to relate to others, his intellectual capacity—to absorb and store information—could ensure a successful career and a happy life. You worry that his potential is going to be wasted.

(c) Language disorders

(i) Expressive language disorder

1 What is it?
A child with this disorder will have difficulty in expressing himself to others. Symptoms vary according to the severity of the condition and the child's age:

- He may have a limited amount of speech and have difficulty in acquiring new words. The structure of his language may be very simple and he may use a restricted variety of sentence types.
- He may speak in short sentences and omit parts of them; there may be mistakes in the vocabulary that he uses.
- His language will not be very fluent; he may speak very quickly and erratically, or excessively slowly and monotonously.
- There will be a marked discrepancy between his ability to express himself and both his non-verbal intelligence and his ability to understand language; the disorder will significantly interfere with his schoolwork and the way in which he communicates with others.

There are two types:

(i) *Acquired* The disorder occurs after a period of normal development and follows either head injury or other medical conditions.
(ii) *Developmental* The child may not begin to speak until very late, and the rate of his language development thereafter will be slower than it should be.

2 *Is it a very common disorder?*
The developmental type is thought to affect 3–5 per cent of children; fewer are affected by the acquired type.

3 *At what age does it appear?*
The acquired type, brought on by head injury or other medical problems, may occur at any time and be sudden. If the developmental type is severe it will be recognised as early as three years, but if mild it may go undetected until early adolescence, when more complex language usually develops.

4 *Can both boys and girls have it?*
The disorder is nearly three times as common in boys as it is in girls.

5 *Is it inherited?*
The developmental type is more likely to occur when there is a family history of communication disorders.

6 *Does the child get better?*
Prospects for a child with the acquired type will depend on the degree of language development he had at the time of acquiring the disorder, on his age, and on the severity of the injury or medical condition. A child with the developmental type will stand a 50 per cent chance of outgrowing it by adolescence. In cases where the condition has been exacerbated by adverse circumstances, there is often rapid improvement when these are resolved.

7 *Could he have another disorder at the same time as this one?*
A child with this disorder may also have a learning disorder. He may also have developmental coordination disorder (dyspraxia). He may have attention-deficit/hyperactivity disorder or suffer from other neurological conditions.

8 *Could the behaviour be caused by something other than expressive language disorder?*
Some of the symptoms may also be displayed by a child with mixed receptive-expressive language disorder (below), autistic disorder or mental disability. In addition:

- He may have a hearing problem.
- He may be suffering from severe adverse circumstances, or be lacking stimulation.
- He may be adversely affected by bilingual family influences.
- He may be suffering from selective mutism (see p. 85).

9 *What will be the effect of the disorder on the child?*

- He will be unable to express himself and in his frustration may become aggressive and disruptive.
- He may develop low self-esteem and exhibit emotional problems.
- Relationships with adults and peers will suffer and his academic progress will be impaired.

10 *How am I likely to feel about a child with this disorder?*
You may feel that you are always in conflict with the child, that he does not appreciate what you want him to do, that he is being deliberately obtuse. You may be very concerned at the lack of progress he is making at school and worried about the relationships he has with his peers.

(ii) Mixed receptive-expressive language disorder

1 *What is it?*
In addition to having problems in expressing himself, a child with this disorder will have difficulty in understanding language.
There are two types—acquired and developmental—and difficulties of expression are similar to those of expressive language disorder (see p. 80):

- The child will be unable to understand words and sentences. In mild cases he may have problems only with certain words or statements, but in more severe cases he may be unable to understand basic vocabulary and simple sentences.

- He may be unable to discriminate sounds, or associate them with symbols.
- He may find it hard to store and recall words or place sounds and symbols in sequence.
- There will be a marked discrepancy between his non-verbal intelligence and his receptive-expressive language ability.
- The disorder will significantly interfere with his progress at school and the way in which he communicates with others.

2 *Is it a very common disorder?*
The developmental type is thought to affect up to 3 per cent of children.

3 *At what age does it appear?*
The acquired type may occur at any time. The developmental type may be recognised before the child is two if it is severe, and is usually evident before the age of four. Milder forms become noticeable when the child is clearly unable to understand his schoolwork.

A form of the disorder that is accompanied by seizures, and known as the Landau-Kleffner syndrome, occurs between the ages of three and nine.

4 *Can both boys and girls have it?*
The disorder is more common in boys than in girls.

5 *Is it inherited?*
A child is more likely to have the developmental type of the disorder if a parent is also a sufferer.

6 *Does the child get better?*
While the language skills of children with the developmental type usually improve, the outcome is not so favourable as it is for those with expressive language disorder. The consequences of this disorder—social rejection, educational failure and low self-esteem—often lead to a lack of friendships as well as to social isolation in adulthood. These problems appear to persist even when the language difficulties begin to dissipate.

Prospects for a child with the acquired type will depend on the degree of language development he had at the time of acquiring the disorder, his age, and the severity of the injury or medical conditions. Severe forms can lead to learning disorders.

7 *Could the child have another disorder at the same time as this one?*
A child with this disorder may also have a learning disorder. He may have developmental coordination disorder (dyspraxia) or attention-deficit/hyperactivity disorder, or suffer from other neurological conditions.

8 *Could the behaviour be caused by something other than mixed receptive-expressive language disorder?*
Some of the symptoms of this disorder may also be displayed by a child with expressive language disorder, phonological disorder (difficulty in classifying sounds), autistic disorder or low intelligence. In addition:

- He may have a hearing problem.
- He may be suffering from severe adverse circumstances, or be lacking stimulation.
- He may be adversely affected by bilingual family influences.
- He may be suffering from selective mutism (see p. 85).

9 *What will be the effect of the disorder on the child?*

- He will be unable to understand what is being said to him: his responses may seem vague and unrelated to the matter being discussed.
- He may appear not to pay attention, or to be confused.
- He may not be able to remember things
- He may not be able to follow instructions.
- He may not be able to sustain a conversation or to take his turn.
- He may be very talkative, or exceptionally quiet.
- His schoolwork and relationships with his peers will be adversely affected.
- Because he is unable to understand others and express himself he may express frustration by becoming aggressive: conversely, he may not even attempt to communicate, and become passive and withdrawn.

- He may develop low self-esteem and exhibit emotional problems.

10 How am I likely to feel about a child with this disorder?
Difficulties in communication may lead to conflict at home and at school. Because he appears on occasions to be able to understand what you are saying you may feel that when he does not respond he is deliberately ignoring you. You may be very concerned at the problems he is having with his schoolwork and the effect of either his passivity or his disruptiveness.

(iii) Selective mutism

1 What is it?
A child with this disorder is capable of speaking and does so, but fails to speak in specific social situations. She must fail to speak for at least a month in order to be said to be suffering from the disorder, but this should not coincide with her first month at school.

2 *Is it a very common disorder?*
It is rare.

3 *At what age does it appear?*
It usually appears before the age of five years, but is often only recognised when the child begins school.

4 *Can both boys and girls have it?*
It is found more frequently in girls.

5 *Is it inherited?*
It is unclear whether the disorder is inherited. Stressful adverse circumstances, particularly where a parent suffers from a disorder, are thought to contribute.

6 *Does the child get better?*
It is extremely rare for the disorder to last beyond six months—but possible. The longer it lasts, the harder it is to treat.

7 *Could she have another disorder at the same time as this one?*
A child with this disorder could also display symptoms of others such as expressive language disorder or mixed receptive-expressive language disorder.

8 *Could the behaviour be caused by something other than selective mutism?*
Some of the symptoms of this disorder may also be displayed by a child with autistic disorder (p. 74), Asperger's disorder (p. 78), schizophrenia (p. 114), mental disability, social phobia (p. 99), depression (p. 112), oppositional defiant disorder (p. 65) or anxiety disorder. In addition:

- She may not speak in certain situations because she stutters or has other communication difficulties.
- She may not speak because she is excessively shy and anxious.
- She may not feel comfortable enough with the language (e.g., if she is an immigrant).
- She may not speak because she has suffered some kind of trauma or because of specific adverse circumstances at home or at school.

9 *What will be the effect of the disorder on the child?*

- She may appear excessively anxious, shy and withdrawn.
- She may have a generally negative attitude and be awkward to control.
- She may have frequent temper tantrums.
- She may have no difficulty in understanding her schoolwork or in reading and writing, but have difficulty in coping with her peers at school.
- While she may speak at home or in other situations with a few people whom she knows, she may not speak in public, with strangers, or when she is at school.
- She may communicate verbally in a limited way, using short utterances, or physically by pushing people and using gestures such as shaking her hands or nodding her head.

10 *How am I likely to feel about a child with this disorder?*
You may feel (wrongly) that the child is consciously refusing to talk. Because of the accompanying awkward behaviour, you may find it difficult to recognise that her mutism is a symptom of fear or anxiety. You may be concerned not only at her not speaking but at the consequences of her behaviour, such as being rejected by her peers and not fulfilling her academic and social potential.

PROBLEMS WITH LEARNING AND COORDINATION

(a) Dyslexia (reading disorder)

1 What is it?
A child with this disorder processes some kinds of information differently from other children; as a result he may, in particular, experience problems in learning to read. There will be a significant discrepancy between his intelligence and his reading performance. He may show signs of having a poor short-term memory, and have difficulty in distinguishing sounds and visual symbols.

2 *Is it a very common disorder?*
It is estimated that up to 10 per cent of children may be affected: 4 per cent are severely affected, and 6 per cent have milder problems.

3 *At what age does it occur?*
Potential problems can be observed at an early age—e.g., delayed development in speech—but the disorder is usually first diagnosed after a child has experienced failure in learning to read.

4 *Can both boys and girls have it?*
Both may suffer from the disorder but four times as many boys as girls are affected.

5 *Is it inherited?*
It is estimated that 70 per cent of those children who have difficulty in learning to read have inherited the disorder.

6 *Does the child get better?*
If the disorder is diagnosed at an early stage, with special help many children can ultimately overcome their problems.

7 *Could he have another disorder at the same time as this one?*
A child with this disorder will also have problems in learning to write. He may have learning difficulties related to mathematics.

Many children who have reading problems also have communication disorders, conduct disorder, oppositional defiant disorder, attention-deficit/hyperactivity disorder, dyspraxia or major depressive disorder. Autistic children may also experience difficulty in learning to read.

8 *Could his learning difficulties be related to anything other than dyslexia?*
Some of the symptoms of this disorder may also be displayed by a child who:

- has difficulty in hearing and seeing, or some other medical problem
- is of low intelligence
- has not had the opportunity to develop pre-reading skills at home—e.g., because of a lack of reading materials or regular conversation
- has a poor teacher
- has a communication disorder, or one of the disorders mentioned in point 7 above.

9 *What will be the effect of the disorder on the child?*

- A child who has difficulty in learning to read may become highly disruptive, or withdraw into himself.
- He may refuse to go to school.
- Both his schoolwork and his relationships with others may be adversely affected.

10 *How am I likely to feel about a child with this disorder?*
You may be frustrated that the future of the child, who is clearly intelligent, is being jeopardised by an inability to master the crucial skill of reading. You may be concerned at the development of disruptive behaviour, or at his negative attitude to anything that involves reading or writing.

(b) Dyspraxia (developmental coordination disorder)

1 *What is it?*
A child with this disorder will display coordination problems: he will have difficulty planning and performing sequences of movements to achieve an objective.

2 *Is it a common disorder?*
It is thought that up to 6 per cent of children may suffer from developmental coordination problems.

3 *At what age does it occur?*
It occurs in early childhood and is usually observed when the child begins to run about or when he attempts tasks that require fine motor skills.

4 *Can both boys and girls have it?*
Both can suffer from the disorder but three times as many boys as girls are affected.

5 *Is it inherited?*
The evidence to support the notion that it is inherited is unclear.

6 *Does the child get better?*
His coordination may improve considerably, or the problem may remain with him in some form for the rest of his life.

7 *Could he have another disorder at the same time as this one?*
A child with this disorder could also suffer from a communication disorder such as expressive language disorder (p. 80) or mixed receptive-expressive language disorder (p. 82).

8 *Could the behaviour be caused by something other than dyspraxia?*
Some of the behaviour of a child with this disorder may also be observed in others, but it would not necessarily mean that they had dyspraxia:

- A child who has difficulty in planning and working through a sequence of movements or tasks may be impulsive and hyperactive, and suffer from attention-deficit/hyperactivity disorder.

- He may have a specific medical condition that is at the root of his difficulties.
- A child who is unresponsive and has difficulty in communicating may be suffering from autistic disorder, or have a communication disorder.
- He may be suffering from Asperger's disorder.
- He may have very low intelligence.

9 What will be the effect of the disorder on the behaviour of the child?

- He may be slow to reach developmental milestones.
- He may appear to lack stamina, and to be ponderous and lethargic in his responses.
- He may be easily distracted by things around him.
- He may have difficulty in communicating either verbally (verbal dyspraxia) or non-verbally; his speech may be unintelligible; his body language and facial responses may be poorly developed.
- Because of his obvious difficulties he may be teased and bullied by other children, and have few friends.
- He may also have difficulty in:

  — *fine motor skills*, e.g., holding and controlling a pencil, using a pair of scissors, naming left and right, performing practical tasks.
  — *gross motor skills*, e.g., running, jumping, hopping; throwing and catching; riding a bicycle; staying still, relaxing, maintaining a steady posture; walking long distances; balancing; changing direction; making slow, precise movements; avoiding bumping into other people.
  — *organisational skills*: following instructions, performing tasks that require a clear sequence to be followed.
  — *learning to read* (muscles around the eye may not work as they should): following the text with his eyes (he will tend to move his whole head), reading more than a few words at a time, including all the words (he will tend to omit some), locating the text on the page (he will tend to lose his place). He will show a general reluctance to read.

— *copying*: locating things on the board, retaining the information, locating the place where the information is to be copied.

10 *How am I likely to feel about a child with this disorder?* You may feel frustrated by the lack of feedback that you receive from your child. His language difficulties may make it very hard to establish rapport with other children or adults. You may be concerned that his disorder will be exacerbated by the teasing and taunting that he receives from his peers.

CONCLUSION

If a child has a physical disability it is perhaps easier, on an emotional level, to cope with any behavioural problems that she presents, since we tend to assume that they are somehow connected with her disability: we feel that we know the reason for her behaviour. But when a child has no obvious physical disability it is much harder to manage her. Because there is no immediately apparent reason for her behaving as she does, we often interpret her behaviour subjectively. We think that she knows exactly what she is doing—and as a consequence we may reject and condemn her.

So far we have considered children who are often thought by those around them to be in full control of their actions: a child with attention-deficit/hyperactivity disorder may be thought to be refusing to concentrate on her work, or selfishly just doing or saying what she wants, when she wants; a child with conduct disorder may be regarded as being wilfully nasty and antisocial; one who has oppositional defiant disorder may be regarded as deliberately touchy, argumentative and annoying. We have also considered, in this chapter, some children, such as those with autistic disorder, whose particular difficulties are more readily accepted as not being of their own doing. We instinctively feel that their behaviour is involuntary—that they have been born with a disability which clearly has a connection with their behaviour. But even with the milder forms of these disorders we may be tempted, in our ignorance, to believe that these children could also improve if only they wanted to.

But it is important not to think of a child's behaviour in this way, since it will inevitably lead you to adopt a negative approach to her problems. I would suggest that, rather than assume that a child is deliberately being uncompliant, we should focus on the notion that she may have a disability. If we do this, and define her problems more accurately, there will be a greater chance of helping her to move forward.

Again, though, a word of caution: if your child has difficulty in relating to others or in communicating with them, or appears to have learning difficulties or problems with her coordination, do resist jumping to the conclusion that she has one of the above disorders. Childhood disorders are all interrelated, and are a great deal more complex than this brief guide can convey. Only a specialist will be able to make a meaningful diagnosis.

6 Disorders relating to Anxiety and Stress; Depression; Schizophrenia

In this chapter we shall consider children whose irritable and demanding behaviour is thought to be primarily caused by anxiety. These children can place great stress upon their parents and teachers, particularly when their anxiety threads through everything they do. When it can be traced to a particular stressful experience it is easier, in a way, to cope with, but often the anxiety will have no apparent cause.

A young child who has a high level of generalised anxiety may be extremely shy and timid. He may cling to his mother and become distressed when she leaves the room. He may have difficulty in sleeping and have regular nightmares. Loud noises may frighten him. He may be afraid of animals and imagine creatures that are going to do him harm. When he is older he may constantly seek reassurance that things are all right; he may regularly need to be convinced that he is doing as well as his peers. As a teenager he may be more worried about his appearance than most. His general level of anxiety may cause him to over-eat, or to stop eating. He may always appear to be tired. He may develop specific fears (phobias), and because of his anxiety he may refuse to go to school or to take part in social activities.

We shall also consider those children who become obsessive and compulsive, and those whose symptoms include tics—who twitch, or produce meaningless words, phrases or sounds. Finally, we shall consider the plight of those children who suffer from depression and schizophrenia—whose illness can, if untreated, lead to suicide.

PROBLEMS TO DO WITH ANXIETY AND STRESS

(a) Generalised anxiety disorder

1 *What is it?*
A child with this disorder will be generally anxious and unable to stop worrying. She may be particularly concerned about her ability to do things—even when she is not being assessed. The focus of her worries may continually change.

2 *Is it a very common disorder?*
It is estimated that 3 per cent of children suffer from it.

3 *At what age does it occur?*
It is thought to occur at any age.

4 *Can both boys and girls have it?*
Although the disorder can occur in both, it is more common in girls.

5 *Is it inherited?*
A child whose parents display the symptoms is more likely to do so herself.

6 *Does the child get better?*
She is likely to suffer from anxiety all her life. The intensity of the symptoms may be exacerbated by actual stressful circumstances.

7 *Could she have another disorder at the same time as this one?*
A child displaying some of the symptoms of this disorder could also be suffering from depression, a phobia, or a substance-related disorder.

8 *Could her behaviour be caused by something other than generalised anxiety disorder?*
Some of the behaviour of a child with this disorder may also be observed in others, but it would not necessarily mean that they had generalised anxiety disorder. A child who is anxious may have a physical illness; or she may have another kind of anxiety disorder:

- She may be anxious about something in particular, in which case she is suffering from specific phobia disorder (see p. 97).
- Her anxiety may be related to a fear of new people and situations—she may have social phobia disorder (see p. 99).
- She may be anxious about being separated from someone who is close to her and be suffering from separation-anxiety disorder (p. 96).
- Her perfectionist behaviour may be an indication of obsessive-compulsive disorder (see p. 103).
- She may be reacting to a traumatic event and be suffering from post-traumatic stress disorder (see p. 101).
- Her anxiousness may indicate depression (p. 112) or schizophrenia (p. 114).
- Her restlessness and inability to concentrate may be an indication of attention-deficit/hyperactivity disorder (p. 59).

9 What will be the effect of the disorder on the child?

- A child with this disorder will be restless and unable to concentrate/stay on task.
- She will have difficulty in sleeping and will be irritable.
- She may tremble or twitch and complain of being tired and having aching muscles.
- Her hands may be clammy; she may sweat or have a dry mouth.
- She may have frequent headaches.
- She may be very concerned about how she performs, and appear to be a perfectionist.
- She may be concerned in particular about punctuality.
- She may worry about the possibility of catastrophic events taking place.
- She may appear permanently on edge.
- She may repeatedly do things to make sure that she *can* do them—and seek reassurance concerning her worries.
- Her relationships with others, as well as her schoolwork, will suffer—she may develop low self-esteem and become either withdrawn or disruptive.

10 How am I likely to feel about a child with this disorder?
You may be on edge because of the state of unrest and tension that she generates. You may feel that there must be something in particular that is causing her to be distressed, and find it hard

to understand that she may be best described as suffering generally from a high level of anxiety that is related to nothing in particular. You may be concerned that, despite being physically well and not mentally impaired, because of this underlying anxiety your child may be unable to fulfil her true academic potential. You may fear that her anxiety and constant demands for reassurance will deter others from associating with her, and that she will become isolated.

(b) Separation-anxiety disorder

1 What is it?

A child with this disorder will suffer distress and become dysfunctional if she is separated from a familiar person, or if she leaves home. The disorder often relates to a major life stress.

2 *Is it a very common disorder?*

It is estimated that 4 per cent of children and adolescents suffer from it.

3 *At what age does it occur?*

It can occur in pre-school children, but is more commonly observed in children who are already at school.

4 *Can both boys and girls have it?*

In the general population, more girls than boys suffer from it.

5 *Is it inherited?*

It is more common in children whose parents also suffer from the disorder, and whose mother may suffer from panic disorder.

6 *Does the child get better?*

The disorder may persist for many years. It is thought that anxiety disorder in childhood may be a precursor to panic disorder in adulthood.

7 *Could she have another disorder at the same time as this one?*

A child displaying some of the symptoms of this disorder could also have generalised anxiety disorder, depression, autistic disorder, Asperger's disorder, a phobia, schizophrenia, panic disorder or attention-deficit/hyperactivity disorder.

8 *Could her behaviour be caused by something other than separation-anxiety disorder?*
Some of the behaviour of a child with this disorder may also be observed in others, but it would not necessarily mean that they had separation-anxiety disorder:

- A child may be anxious because of family problems.
- She may be ill.
- She may be worried about her schoolwork.
- She may be being bullied at school, or finding it difficult to relate to others.
- She may be over-needed and overprotected at home.

9 *What will be the effect of the disorder on the child?*
When separated from a person who is close to her or from her home, she may become unhappy and withdrawn. She may:

- feel that she has been rejected and that nobody loves her
- express her anger by becoming aggressive
- become very demanding and need constant attention
- fear and despair that she will never be reunited with her carer
- fear being on her own
- be unable to sleep away from home unless her carer is in close proximity
- have nightmares, or complain of being ill
- need to sleep with her parents
- have difficulty in concentrating and fail in her schoolwork
- refuse to go to school
- be unable to go anywhere on her own
- be unwilling to spend time at a friend's house, or go on a school outing.

10 *How am I likely to feel about a child with this disorder?*
You may be ambivalent about your child's lack of independence: you may take pride in the fact that your family is close-knit, but worry about her inability to cope without you.

(c) Specific phobia disorder

1 *What is it?*
A child with this disorder will react with fear and anxiety when she is in the presence of a particular object or in a certain situation, or when she anticipates being so.

The disorder has various subtypes:

(i) *Animal type* The child fears animals or insects.
(ii) *Natural-environment type* She fears heights, water, storms, etc.
(iii) *Blood/injection type* She reacts with anxiety to blood, or to receiving an injection.
(iv) *Situational type* She fears a specific situation, such as crossing a bridge or using an elevator.
(v) *Other type* She reacts with anxiety to other situations or events.

2 *Is it a very common disorder?*
Many children have phobias, but it is rare for them to be so severe as to be diagnosed as a disorder.

3 *At what age does it occur?*
It can occur in very young children, but as most children occasionally display the symptoms in some form or another, it is more easily diagnosed when they are older.

4 *Can both boys and girls have it?*
Both can have the disorder. With most of the subtypes girls are more likely to be sufferers, but more boys have a fear of heights.

5 *Is it inherited?*
A child is more likely to have a phobia if one of her parents also has—this is especially true with the blood/injection type.

6 *Does the child get better?*
The symptoms of the disorder usually diminish during adolescence; they may, however, persist into adulthood and if they do so are unlikely to dissipate.

7 *Could she have another disorder at the same time as this one?*
A child displaying some of the symptoms of this disorder could also have anxiety disorder, social phobia, post-traumatic stress disorder, obsessive-compulsive disorder or separation-anxiety disorder.

8 *Could her behaviour be caused by something other than specific phobia disorder?*
Some of the behaviour of a child with this disorder may also be observed in others, but it would not necessarily mean that they had specific phobia. It is normal for all children to experience a certain degree of apprehension when faced with new objects or situations.

9 *What will be the effect of the disorder on the child?*

- She may avoid the specific objects or situations that cause her problems—or endure them with distress.
- While an older child may be aware of the irrational nature of her fears and be able to express them, a young child will not: she may respond by having tantrums; she may cry or cling to her carer.
- Because of her phobia the child may not be able to participate in usual peer activities and school events.
- She may be deterred from going to school, and her relationships with others may suffer.

10 How am I likely to feel about a child with this disorder?
You may feel that your child's phobia severely restricts what you are able to do with her. You may feel that her fears are adversely affecting the life of your family. You may worry that her phobia will persist into adulthood and present problems when she goes to work or college.

(d) Social phobia disorder

1 What is it?
A child with this disorder will have a fear of social situations where he is exposed to unfamiliar people or situations in which his performance may be scrutinised. He will fear that in such situations he will suffer embarrassment or humiliation. He may fear a specific situation, or suffer from generalised social phobia if he is fearful in a range of situations. He will experience the fear in the presence both of adults and of his peers.

In normal circumstances the child will behave appropriately and will have no difficulty in coping with situations or generally relating to others.

2 *Is it a very common disorder?*
It is estimated that 3–13 per cent of people suffer from it. The severity of their difficulties varies according to the type of phobia. The number of people requiring intensive treatment is small.

3 *At what age does it occur?*
Young children over the age of two and a half may display the symptoms, but the disorder is more common among teenagers who may have been timid or shy when they were younger. It may follow a traumatic or stressful event at any age.

4 *Can both boys and girls have it?*
Both can suffer from the disorder.

5 *Is it inherited?*
A child is more likely to suffer from the disorder if a parent is also a sufferer.

6 *Does the child get better?*
The disorder may dissipate in childhood. However, a child with the disorder is likely to be susceptible to it for the remainder of his life—the degree of his suffering will depend on how much his lifestyle requires him to be exposed to the circumstances that he finds stressful.

7 *Could he have another disorder at the same time as this one?*
A child displaying some of the symptoms of this disorder could also have obsessive-compulsive disorder (p. 103), mood disorder or substance-related disorders (p. 67).

8 *Could his behaviour be caused by something other than social phobia disorder?*
Some of the behaviour of a child with this disorder may also be observed in others, but it would not necessarily mean that they had social phobia:

- A child may avoid social settings because he has separation-anxiety disorder and is afraid to leave his mother.
- A child who fears embarrassment or humiliation may have a generalised or specific anxiety disorder, which makes him worry about his performance even when others are not involved.

- A child who avoids others or taking part in activities may do so because he suffers from autistic disorder and has no interest in socialising.
- He may have a physical impairment which deters him from becoming involved.
- He may be ashamed of his physical appearance, or of his intellectual ability.
- A child who is fearful of people or situations in which he may be in the limelight may be suffering from depression (see p. 112).
- He may be taking drugs.

9 What will be the effect of the disorder on the child?

- He will be unable to take a full part in all activities.
- He may be shy, lack confidence and be unable to play successfully with his peers.
- He may be excessively timid and have few social skills.
- He may perform poorly at school.
- He may refuse to go to school.
- He may have few interests and contacts outside of the home.

10 How am I likely to feel about a child with this disorder?
Because of your child's ability to be quite sociable, you may be frustrated when he displays his fear in certain situations. You may be worried that his schoolwork is suffering and that relationships with his peers are deteriorating.

(e) Post-traumatic stress disorder

1 What is it?
A child with this disorder will have been exposed to a specific stressful experience in which he or others may have suffered physically, or been at risk:

- He may have witnessed or heard about the death of, or injury to, someone he knows, or be aware of the possibility that such an event might take place.
- He may have been involved in a natural disaster such as a flood or a violent storm, or have been the victim of abuse.
- He may have been inappropriately exposed to sexual activity.
- He may have been involved in a car accident.
- He may have had a life-threatening illness.

2 *Is it a very common disorder?*
It is estimated to afflict 1–14 per cent of people during their lifetime.

3 *At what age does it occur?*
It can occur at any age.

4 *Can both boys and girls have it?*
Both suffer equally from the disorder.

5 *Is it inherited?*
Other disorders that are thought to be inherited may exacerbate a child's reaction to a specific stressful event.

6 *Does the child get better?*
The disorder usually occurs immediately after the traumatic event, but delayed symptoms can occur months, or even years, later. It usually lasts no longer than three months, but chronic cases can last longer. The speed of recovery will depend on the severity of the traumatic event, how long it lasted and how involved the child was. It will also depend on the degree of support that he receives from his present circumstances.

7 *Could he have another disorder at the same time as this one?*
There is no other disorder that is commonly found to coexist with this one.

8 *Could his behaviour be caused by something other than post-traumatic stress disorder?*
Some of the behaviour of a child with this disorder may also be observed in others, but would not necessarily mean that they had post-traumatic stress disorder:

- A child who is disturbed and agitated before the traumatic event may have another anxiety disorder or suffer from depression.
- A child's intrusive thoughts may not be connected to a traumatic event and may indicate that the is suffering from obsessive-compulsive disorder (below).
- His 'flashbacks' may be better interpreted as other disturbances which might indicate that he is suffering from substance-abuse disorder (p. 67) or schizophrenia (p. 114).

9 What will be the effect of the disorder on the child?

- He may become disorganised or agitated.
- His behaviour may generally deteriorate, and he may complain of headaches and stomach aches.
- He may relive the event by repeating it in play in which the trauma, or aspects of it, are the central theme.
- The trauma may be re-experienced in dreams and give him nightmares.
- He may overreact when he is surprised by a loud sound or by somebody suddenly appearing.
- He may appear to be detached as he relives the experience in his mind.
- He may avoid anything connected with the event, and when exposed to things that remind him of it he may become agitated and distressed.
- He may appear 'flat' and unresponsive to everything around him.
- He may complain of feeling detached and uninterested in things, and of having few feelings for anyone.
- He may feel that he will not live long.
- He may be unable to concentrate and stay on task.

10 How am I likely to feel about a child with this disorder?
You may be surprised at his behaviour and fail to connect it with an event that happened a long time ago.

(f) Obsessive-compulsive disorder

1 What is it?
A child with this disorder will have either obsessions or compulsions, or both. When he is older he may recognise the pointlessness of his behaviour but be unable to do anything about it; he may feel that his obsessions and compulsions are out of his control.

- *Obsessions* Obsessions can take many forms. Commonly, the child may have persistent thoughts about becoming dirty, or repeated doubts about whether he has or has not done something. He may need everything to be in a precise order. His obsession will be more than excessive worrying about a particular concern, such as some schoolwork or having to keep things tidy.

- *Compulsion* To alleviate the distress caused by his obsession he may repeatedly wash his hands, check that he has done what he should have, keep placing objects in a certain order, or count and recount them.

2 *Is it a very common disorder?*
Amongst anxiety disorders in children, this is one of the more common. It is estimated that 2.5 per cent of children may suffer from it.

3 *At what age does it occur?*
It may occur in childhood but is more likely to be first observed in adolescence.

4 *Can both boys and girls have it?*
This disorder is suffered equally by both.

5 *Is it inherited?*
A child is more likely to have the disorder if a parent is a sufferer.

6 *Does the child get better?*
In most cases the symptoms come and go; it is thought that they may be triggered by stressful situations. The disorder can be chronic and disabling, and it is estimated that only 50 per cent of sufferers recover.

7 *Could he have another disorder at the same time as this one?*
A child displaying some of the symptoms of this disorder could also be suffering from depression, a phobia (p. 97) or an eating disorder (p. 109). Many children with Tourette's disorder (p. 106) also suffer from obsessive-compulsive disorder.

8 *Could his behaviour be caused by something other than obsessive-compulsive disorder?*
Some of the behaviour of a child with this disorder may also be observed in others, but it would not necessarily mean that they had obsessive-compulsive disorder:

- A child who has intrusive, repeating thoughts and images may be suffering from one of a number of mental disorders.
- His repeated thoughts of worthlessness may indicate that he is suffering from depression.
- If he is constantly worried about something (e.g., to do with school, or a friend) he may be suffering from generalised anxiety.
- If he has a repeated fear he may be suffering from a phobia.
- If he has repeated concerns and, when older, is unable to recognise his problem he may be suffering from schizophrenia.
- If he repeatedly drinks alcohol or eats excessively, and enjoys doing so, this may indicate that he has a substance-abuse (p. 67) or an eating disorder.

9 *What will be the effect of the disorder on the child?*

- He may spend a large part of his time tidying his belongings.
- He may repeatedly count them and place them in a certain way.
- He may go through a number of other rituals.
- He may be distressed whenever he becomes dirty, and avoid playing games because of this.
- He may worry about the possibility of getting dirty or of his possessions being out of order.
- He may dislike touching things or shaking hands with people.
- Persistent thoughts, fears and apprehensions may prevent him from taking part in normal school activities or doing his work.
- When he is older and aware of his problem, but unable to feel that he is in control of it, he may become depressed.

10 How am I likely to feel about a child with this disorder?
When he is young you may sense that his behaviour is a sign of some deep-seated anxiety. His constant ordering and counting and his fear of becoming contaminated by 'dirt' may appear to indicate gross insecurity and a need for control, and be a great worry to you. When he is older and can express his own distress at these behaviours you may feel that he should be able to do something about them. You may find it hard to accept that he cannot.

PHYSICAL MANIFESTATIONS OF DISTRESS

(a) Tic disorders (including Tourette's disorder)

1 What are they?

A child with a tic disorder will experience recurrent sudden, rapid movements in part of his body, or irresistible urges to vocalise. There are three tic disorders:

(i) *Transient tic disorder* In this type, the tics occur many times each day and persist for at least four weeks. They last for no longer than twelve months. The tics are usually confined to the eyes, face, neck or upper body. Commonly, children suffer from the disorder between the ages of three and ten, and boys are at greater risk than girls.
(ii) *Chronic motor or vocal tic disorder* A child with this disorder will have either motor (movement) tics or vocal tics, but not both. They will occur many times a day and will be evident over a period of more than a year. Usually the tics are confined to the eyes, face, head, neck and upper body. The disorder can occur at any time in childhood and is suffered by both boys and girls. It can persist into adulthood, where it most commonly manifests itself during times of stress. The symptoms are not so severe as those experienced by a child with Tourette's disorder.
(iii) *Tourette's disorder* This is the most severe of the tic disorders. The child will have a number of motor tics and at least one vocal tic. The tics will occur many times a day and will be evident over a period of more than a year. Their nature and severity change over time. Motor tics commonly affect the upper body and the head, but the range is wide and any part of the body can be affected; vocal tics can include certain words, clicks, grunts, barks, sniffs and coughs, and in a small number of cases, obscenities.

There are four kinds of tics, the intensity of which can range from mild (and barely noticeable) to severe (and extremely frightening to others) and is likely to increase in stressful circumstances:

1 simple motor tics: e.g., head-jerking, blinking, pulling faces, shrugging, coughing.
2 simple vocal tics: e.g., squeaking, grunting, sniffing, throat-clearing, barking.
3 complex motor tics: e.g., brushing hair with arm, facial ges-

tures, smelling objects, jumping, touching, tapping; more rarely, potentially self-injurious behaviour such as slapping, punching face, biting wrists.
4 complex vocal tics: e.g., repeating meaningless words and sounds or those last heard, blurting out obscenities.

2 *Is it a very common disorder?*
Many children experience transient tics, but it is rare for a child to have a chronic tic disorder.

3 *At what age does it occur?*
It can occur in children as young as two, but is more common in childhood or early adolescence. Young children may be unaware of their tics, but those over the age of ten are usually conscious of them (they may even describe them as voluntary responses to something that they find unpleasant).

4 *Can both boys and girls have it?*
Although both can suffer, the disorder is more common in boys.

5 *Is it inherited?*
A child with a parent who is a sufferer is more susceptible to developing the disorder.

6 *Does the child get better?*
The disorder usually remains with him for the rest of his life. The worst symptoms commonly occur between the ages of nine and fifteen but may diminish during adolescence and early adulthood. Vocal tics tend to diminish more rapidly than motor tics. In a few cases the symptoms disappear altogether.

7 *Could he have another disorder at the same time as this one?*
A child with this disorder could also have attention-deficit disorder, anxiety disorder, obsessive-compulsive disorder or a learning disorder.

8 *Could his behaviour be caused by something other than a tic disorder?*
Some of the behaviour of a child with this disorder may also be observed in others, but it would not necessarily mean that they

had a tic disorder. Tic disorders are thought by many to be strongly related to a number of other disorders:

- A child's repetitive movements may be related to a form of autistic disorder, or he may be suffering from obsessive-compulsive disorder.
- His tics could be related to a form of schizophrenia (p. 114).
- They could also be linked to medication that he is receiving for another disorder.

9 *What will be the effect of the disorder on the child?*

- He will display symptoms outlined in the description of tics (above), and symptoms of those disorders, mentioned in point 7 above, from which he may also suffer.
- He will be embarrassed, and become self-conscious.
- He may become depressed.
- Relationships with others will suffer—he may be teased and bullied, and his schoolwork will be adversely affected.
- He will find it hard to make friends.
- In severe cases he may be unable to do his schoolwork because of the tics.

10 How am I likely to feel about a child with this disorder?
While most children with this disorder are loving and affectionate they tend to display a range of behavioural problems associated with other disorders (see point 7 above). You may therefore feel frustrated at not being able to decide how far his demanding and disruptive behaviour is connected to his Tourette's disorder, or how much it is related to another possible disorder.

His tics may be extremely annoying: tension may build up within your family and you may feel constantly on edge. You may be concerned that the disorder will result in your child becoming increasingly isolated, and that as a result he may become either excessively withdrawn or actively involved in anti-social activities.

* * *

Other disorders (beyond the scope of this book to discuss more fully) which are thought by some to be physical manifestations of anxiety include the following.

(b) Eating disorders

A child whose anxiety centres on her appearance may experiment with diets or refuse to eat certain nutritional foods—with adverse effects.

Anorexia nervosa

A child going into adolescence may have a fear of becoming fat. She may begin by dieting to become attractive, but be unable to appreciate that she is becoming thin and haggard. She may end up experiencing a loss of self-control—and in an attempt to regain it, she may persist further with the diet and either subject herself to rigorous exercise or misuse laxatives in order to reduce her weight. She may also deliberately vomit. Her general lifestyle may reflect this excessive need for control; she may think rather rigidly; she may become obsessional/compulsive about food. She may suffer from depression (p. 112). She will take little notice of what others say—even those close to her. The disorder can be chronic and unremitting.

Bulimia

An adolescent going into adulthood may have all the symptoms of anorexia nervosa (above), but she may not only vomit but gorge herself with food, consuming enormous amounts in a short time. Following this there may be a period when she fasts so as to re-lose her weight. The disorder can abate and then reappear.

(c) Self-injurious behaviour

A child who is anxious and has low self-esteem may punish himself or try to take control by self-injuring: he may, for example, cut his arms or burn the back of his hand with a cigarette. He may attempt suicide.

(d) Enuresis (wetting)

Although there are a number of medical reasons why a child may be unable to keep dry, there are also strong associations between enuresis and psychiatric disorders—including anxiety. Many children have problems keeping dry during the night, and some suffer during the day. For the wetting to be regarded as significant, the child should either be over five years old and be wet at least twice a week over a period of three months, or be severely distressed and impaired by the condition. There are two types of enuresis:

(i) *Primary* The child has never been able to keep dry.
(ii) *Secondary* He has become enuretic after a dry period. The latter usually occurs between the ages of five and seven and is uncommon after the age of eleven. More boys than girls suffer with secondary enuresis. The child may begin wetting following the birth of a brother or sister or after he has suffered an injury or witnessed a traumatic event. A high percentage of the children who suffer from this condition come from families where one of the parents had a similar problem when he or she was a child. It is so distressing that it may be regarded as a cause of disturbance rather than the result of another disorder, but it can be treated successfully in nearly all cases.

(e) Encopresis (soiling)

Almost all children will soil themselves at some time or another: for it to be regarded as significant it will occur after the age of four and will be evident at least once a month over a period of three months. Although there are medical reasons for soiling, it is also thought to be associated with anxiety and stress.

As with enuresis, it is not clear whether the condition is a disorder in itself which, because of its social implications, can create other severe problems for the child, or whether it is a symptom of another disorder. Many children who experience delayed development in language and coordination also suffer from this condition, as do children who are mentally disabled. There are four kinds of children who soil:

(i) those who are able to control their bowels but who either lose control when faced with stress, such as the birth of a sibling or admission to hospital (control is regained when the stress dissipates), or choose to deposit their faeces in inappropriate places or smear them on walls and clothing—seemingly to cause maximum irritation.
(ii) those who may be mentally or physically disabled and

unaware of their problem, and deposit their faeces in clothing whether they are at home or elsewhere.
(iii) those who suffer from diarrhoea when they are frightened or put in stressful situations
(iv) those who have toilet phobia—a fear of the toilet or of even going near it.

More boys than girls suffer from encopresis, and the condition is harder to treat in older children. It inevitably means that the child is ostracised, and that he may feel rejected by the anger and frustration of those who care for him.

(f) Sleep disorders
There are many forms of sleep disorder, all of which are thought to be associated with anxiety. While it is thought that a child is more likely to have a sleep disorder if one of his parents was, or is, a sufferer, night terrors and nightmares are thought to be linked to post-traumatic stress disorder (p. 101).

(i) *Sleepwalking* It is estimated that 30 per cent of children have walked in their sleep at least once and that 2.5 per cent do so regularly. For a child to be regarded as having a sleepwalking disorder the walking should take place regularly and the child be clearly distressed by it or by its practical implications. It may, for example, prevent her from staying overnight with friends or from inviting them to stay with her. She may respond only in a limited way to others when she is walking, and it will be difficult to wake her up. When she has woken she will be back to normal after a few minutes and will not remember the episode. Both boys and girls suffer from this problem, but it usually disappears by the time they are fifteen.
(ii) *Night terrors* A child suffering from a night terror will suddenly wake up in a highly agitated state. He may cry out and express such intense terror that his parents will be extremely alarmed. He will be hard to comfort, but (unlike with a nightmare, see below) he will not be able to describe a dream, and he will have no recollection of why he woke and called out. The disorder usually begins between the ages of four and twelve and resolves itself during adolescence. It is more commonly experienced by boys than by girls.
(iii) *Nightmares* Most children experience a nightmare at least

once. They usually begin between the ages of three and five. When they recur to the extent that the child is becoming persistently distressed—e.g., several times a week—they are regarded as a disorder. After a frightening dream the child will wake and become fully alert; he will be able to describe the dream in detail. Most children grow out of nightmares, but occasionally they continue to suffer from them into adulthood.

(iv) *Head-banging/rocking* Children at a very young age may rock themselves or bang their heads as they go to sleep. If this becomes vigorous and potentially harmful it can be alarming for their parents. However, the rituals are quite common in mild forms, and usually do not persist into later childhood.

DEPRESSION

It is estimated that as many as 10 per cent of children experience mood disorders before the age of twelve, and that up to 25 per cent of people suffer from some form of depression during their lifetime. There are four main kinds of mood disorder, all of which are interrelated. Each has its own unique combination of different kinds of mood 'episodes'. (Because of the complexity of the subject—there are many subtypes which I won't mention here—we will briefly note the four main groups.)

1 Major depressive disorder*

A child with this disorder will experience one or more *major depressive episodes*. They will last at least two weeks, during which she may:

- appear 'flat', distinctly unhappy and irritable
- be unable to find pleasure in anything
- express feelings of worthlessness
- express feelings of guilt
- be excessively tired and lack energy
- experience difficulty in sleeping and a loss of appetite
- have suicidal thoughts
- lose or gain weight
- become aggressive and disrespectful of authority
- deteriorate in her school performance.

The disorder can occur at any age and is experienced by both boys and girls; during adolescence twice as many girls have it. A child with a parent who suffers from it is much more likely to have the disorder than others. She may experience a single episode, or episodes may recur. The more they recur, the greater the likelihood of the disorder persisting. It will affect the child's performance at school and her relationships with others.

A younger child with the disorder is likely also to suffer from attention-deficit/hyperactivity disorder (p. 59) or anxiety disorder (p. 94); an older child may suffer from substance-related disorder (p. 67). Any sufferer may be at risk of committing suicide: it is estimated that 15 per cent of those with the disorder end their own lives.

A major depressive episode is often preceded by *dysthymic disorder*.

2 Dysthymic disorder

A child with this disorder will, roughly speaking, display the symptoms of a major depressive disorder (above), but they will persist over a period of at least two years. The symptoms will be less severe, and because of their persistence over a long period the condition may often go unrecognised. Dysthymic disorder is a good predictor of major depressive disorder, and a child's condition may alternate between the two.

Approximately 3 per cent of children are thought to have the disorder, and it can occur at any age. Both boys and girls can suffer from it, and they are more likely to do so if one of their parents has major depressive disorder. Children who have attention-deficit/hyperactivity disorder or conduct disorder, or who have low intelligence, often also suffer from this disorder.

3 Bipolar I disorder

A child with this disorder will suffer from one or more manic episodes, or mixed episodes. These occur most often either immediately before or after a major depressive episode (see p. 112):

Manic episode A child who has a manic episode will, for at least a week, appear to be on an exaggerated 'high'. She may have an inflated sense of her own importance, speak incessantly, have less need for sleep, be full of ideas—but flit from one thing to another. She may live life to the full—excessively so, in fact, and generally appear agitated. Her mood may alternate between this euphoric and expansive state and one of irritability.

Mixed episode A child who has a mixed episode will rapidly alternate between manic episodes and major depressive episodes.

Bipolar 1 disorder is estimated to affect 0.4–1.6 per cent of the population. It can affect both boys and girls, and they stand a much greater chance of suffering from this or from either bipolar 2 disorder or major depressive disorder if one of their parents is also a sufferer. The condition recurs throughout a child's life. She may experience failure at school and exhibit antisocial behaviour; she will also be at greater risk of committing suicide. Children with the disorder often also exhibit the symptoms of attention-deficit/hyperactivity disorder, social phobia or substance-related disorders.

4 Bipolar 2 disorder

A child with this condition will experience one or more major depressive episodes (p. 112) and at least one hypomanic episode:

Hypomanic episode This has the same characteristics as a manic episode (above), but the child's symptoms will not be so severe—she will not be so incapacitated by them.

The disorder is suffered by approximately 0.5 per cent of the population. Both boys and girls can have it, though it is thought that more women are afflicted than men. Children of parents with the disorder are most likely to suffer from it; and they are also more likely to experience bipolar 1 disorder and major depressive disorder. A child with the condition may experience failure at school and is likely also to suffer from substance-related disorder, attention-deficit/hyperactivity disorder, or social phobia.

SCHIZOPHRENIA*

1 What is it?

A child who suffers from this disorder will have problems with his thought processes. He will have difficulty in perceiving things and will have emotional problems. The symptoms will last for at least a month and will have been evident in some form over a period of at least six months.

There are various subtypes (and other, associated, disorders), each with its own characteristics.

2 *Is it a very common disorder?*
It is rare in children but cases increase in number during adolescence. It is estimated that up to 1 per cent of adults suffer from it during their lifetime.

3 *At what age does it occur?*
The disorder can occur in young children, but is more commonly diagnosed among those in their late teens.

4 *Can both boys and girls have it?*
Both boys and girls can suffer from it. It is unclear whether they are at equal risk, but it is thought that boys who suffer from it do so at an earlier age than girls.

5 *Is it inherited?*
A child is more likely to suffer from the disorder if one of his parents does, and he is at an even greater risk if they are both sufferers.

6 *Does the child get better?*
Few, if any, children with the disorder recover completely. Symptoms recur, and in between active phases a child may continue to have milder 'residual' problems. There is a high risk of a child with the disorder committing suicide, especially if he has previously been performing very well and has had high expectations for the future. It is estimated that 10 per cent of sufferers end their own lives.

7 *Could he have another disorder at the same time as this one?*
A child with this disorder could display the symptoms of a number of others, such as anxiety disorder or mood disorder, though none is specifically associated with it.

8 *Could his behaviour be caused by something other than schizophrenia?*
Some of the behaviour of a child with this disorder may also be

observed in others, but it would not necessarily mean that they had schizophrenia. Distinguishing schizophrenia from some other conditions is particularly difficult. The following are only a few examples:

- A child's delusions and hallucinations may be related to a substance-related disorder, anxiety disorder or conduct disorder.
- His apathy and his flattened responses may be an indication of a mood disorder.
- The disturbance in his language may indicate that he has a communication disorder.
- His remoteness may indicate that he has autistic disorder.
- His inability to stay on task may indicate that he has attention-deficit/hyperactivity disorder.

9 What will be the effect of the disorder on the child?
He will suffer from:

- *Delusions*
  —He may wrongly believe that he is being persecuted, that gestures and comments are aimed at him or that people are always watching him.
  —He may believe that his thoughts and actions are being controlled by someone else.
  —His beliefs will be strong and unreasonable, and may appear bizarre.
- *Hallucinations*
  —He may imagine voices which criticise and threaten him; they may give a running commentary on his behaviour.
  —He may have visions, or imagine smells and tastes.
- *Disorganised thoughts*
  —He may flit from one topic of conversation to another, seemingly unrelated, one; he will not be able to maintain the thread of a conversation.
  —His answers to questions may be totally unconnected with the questions.
  —His speech may be garbled and unintelligible.
- *Disorganised behaviour*
  —He may be unable to sustain attention and complete tasks.
  —He may not be able to perform necessary daily routines.

—His behaviour may appear unusual and bizarre.

- *Flattened reactions*
  —He may appear remote and unreachable.
  —When he responds he may do so in a robotic monotone.
  —His response may be very brief and empty.
  —He may appear to have little if any interest in anything or anybody.
- *Catatonic behaviour*
  —He may appear to be in a stupor.
  —He may be mute.
  —He may 'freeze', or become excessively active for no apparent reason.
  —He may adopt bizarre physical postures.

Depending on the severity of the disorder, when it began and its principal symptoms, his school performance and his relationships with others will be adversely affected. He may be unable to complete his schooling. He may develop feelings of helplessness and despair, and contemplate suicide.

10 *How am I likely to feel about a child with this disorder?*
You may have been alarmed at the inexplicable, bizarre behaviour of your child. You may be embarrassed by his unsociable behaviour and inability to conform. You may feel—though your fear will be unfounded, since a person with schizophrenia is no more likely to harm others than anyone else—that the disorder will make him a greater danger to yourself or to others. You may be apprehensive at the thought that it will lead him into feelings of helplessness and despair—with fatal consequences.

Your distress may be exacerbated by the knowledge that the disorder will always jeopardise your child's prospects.

CONCLUSION

Childhood disorders can all too often go unrecognised, but the consequences cannot be overestimated.

The fact that a child is suffering from anxiety may easily go undetected; his demanding and self-centred behaviour may be wrongly thought to be an indication that he can clearly look after his own interests. If his underlying anxiety is not recognised and his needs met, he may develop oppositional defiant disorder and later conduct disorder. He may become alienated from society and drift into a life of crime. A child with depression may have always presented as rather 'flat' and passive—this may be considered to be 'how he is'. But if his symptoms are not recognised for what they are, his feeling that nobody cares will only be confirmed and he may despair to the point of contemplating ending his life.

* * *

In this chapter we have considered the nature of anxiety in children and how it leads to serious problems; we have considered illnesses such as depression and schizophrenia which can lead to serious incapacity, and even suicide. Now that you have looked at some of the disorders that can occur in childhood and adolescence, you will hopefully be more appreciative of the difficulties that your child may be experiencing. As I said earlier, don't despair at the thought that his problems may never be completely resolved. Even with serious illnesses such as depression or schizophrenia, which tend to stay with a person, there is a great deal that can be done to alleviate his suffering. With specialist help—and if you detect his problems at an early age—there is a good chance that his symptoms will be controlled and that he will be able to lead a fulfilling life.

In Part Three we shall consider some general approaches that might be adopted at home and at school, and take a brief look at some of the techniques that may be employed by specialists.

Part Three

WHAT CAN BE DONE?

7 At Home

In Part One we assessed whether you might need to refer your child to a specialist. In this part of the book we shall begin by examining how you can get help, and what form this may take. We will then consider what *you* can do at home to help your child achieve his full potential. Although there are special treatment approaches for the various disorders, there are also some general guiding principles that apply to most cases, and any specialist that you see may be interested in how far you have followed these.

A key to success is for parents and teachers to work together—to regard themselves as part of a multidisciplinary team with a common purpose. This chapter and the next, which separately discuss approaches to be taken by parents and by teachers, should therefore be read by both.

SEEK HELP

Teacher, doctors, support groups

If your child's behaviour concerns you and he does not yet attend school, consult your family doctor. If he is already at school, first talk to his teacher, and in the light of what you have read in this book assess what has already been done for him. Ensure that the Code of Practice (ask the school's Special Educational Needs Coordinator (SENCO) about this) has been followed, and that your child is well placed in his present class and school. Check that the suggested strategies for teachers (see p. 153) have been appropriately followed.

If adjustments at home and in his school setting have already been implemented and have had no effect, consult your family doctor. Either he or the school may suggest that your child see an educational or clinical psychologist, or a child and adolescent psychiatrist. If your child's problems appear to centre on difficulties at home you may be visited by a social worker; or it may be suggested that a trained counsellor should become involved. Often this wide-ranging group of specialists work as a multidisciplinary team, pooling their resources to ensure that all aspects of a child's difficulties have been considered.

Don't be deterred from taking action because of the thought of being descended upon by so many experts. As I said earlier, they are interested only in joining you in your search for a solution. To begin with, they will feel as unsure about things as you do. Your responses to the twenty questions (p. 8) and the thinking you will have done after reading this book will have prepared you well to meet them.

If teachers and doctors don't feel that it is necessary to involve a specialist and you are still concerned, you could make an appointment with a private consultant (see Appendix A). If you cannot afford a private consultation, or if you want details of those in your area, contact your Citizens' Advice Bureau or local library for advice. If you explain your child's particular problem they may not only provide you with this information but put you in touch with your nearest parent support group. There are many support groups for a variety of childhood disorders: they are a source not only of information and advice but of invaluable emotional and practical support. Specialist associations and charitable organisations also exist, to help both parents and children who suffer from a range of physical, intellectual and emotional problems (see Appendix A for sources of information and advice).

Specialists: tests, interviews, medical examination, treatment

Specialists may require your child to undertake tests that will provide them with an indication not only of his intellectual ability and learning processes, but of the way he thinks and feels about himself—and, for example, whether he may be suffering from a particular disorder such as depression. You too, and other members of your family, may be interviewed, in an attempt to discover the family's history and how your child fits into its dynamics.

He may also be physically examined, since some disorders are caused by physical conditions. They can, for example, be caused by prescribed or non-prescribed drugs, lead poisoning, infection, head injury or abnormal hormone secretion. By administering tests and by interviewing those who play some part in the child's life, specialists will not only be able to define the problem more clearly, but be able to establish where they are starting from. If your child has a disorder, however mild, it is important to be able to assess whether the treatment he receives is working. Measurement of his progress will be taken from these baseline tests and interviews.

The diagnosis and treatment of childhood disorders is an extremely complex process. A child may be behaving badly for a variety of reasons, and, in addition, may be suffering from more than one disorder. Treatment is therefore to a large extent by trial and error. So don't expect any quick-fix single solutions.

Although in many instances much can be achieved in a short time—with dramatic and almost immediate improvements to be seen in some cases—nothing can be guaranteed. You must bear in mind that your child's development and life situation will constantly change, so that you will inevitably have to make regular adjustments to his treatment programme. In this fluctuating state of affairs, when you are dealing with 'so-called' specialists, don't be tempted to adopt a 'they don't know what they're doing' attitude. Although there may be an element of truth in this, the chances of your child being given the correct treatment will to a large extent depend on how far you support their various recommendations. In relation to the advice you are given by the specialists, you will only harm your child's prospects if you cast the smallest doubt in his mind about the treatment he is receiving. If you have any concerns, discuss them with the specialist—privately. And allow her to decide when it is appropriate to involve your child in any form of decision-making.

An alternative school placement?

If you are considering whether he should remain in his present school, first check to see that everything possible has been done to help him (see Chapter 8). But don't preclude the possibility that he may benefit by moving elsewhere: if he remains, the situation may only worsen. If he is disruptive or regularly truanting and has had a number of fixed-term exclusions, he is probably greatly disliked and will have developed a negative image of himself. If this is the case he will stand a greater chance of success in another school. If he is continually depressed it could be that he is being bullied and that a fresh start elsewhere is the only answer for him.

Each local education authority has a Behaviour Support Plan which provides details of the provision it makes for pupils who have behavioural problems. A copy of this will be provided on request, or will be available in your local library.

If your child cannot remain in his present school, he may be provided with emergency provision in the form of home tuition: he may be visited in your home by a teacher, until a suitable placement can be found. But the longer the child is at home, living his own lifestyle and receiving personal tutoring, the harder it will be for him to return—you should therefore press hard for a placement to be acquired as soon as possible. An interim measure, to prevent his fear of returning from intensifying, may be to make some arrangement whereby he is visited by other pupils or teachers from his present school.

It may be suggested that your child be placed in a small unit attached to his school or in a 'pupil referral unit'. These special facilities are designed to help children overcome temporary problems and to assess where they might best be placed. Again, if this is the case with your child, do be alert to the risk of his remaining too long in this kind of 'temporary' facility. If he has Special Educational Needs it may be suggested that he attend a Day Special School. This kind of school will have teachers who are trained to deal with children who have learning and behavioural problems. Classes will be small and the children will often have access to one-to-one supervision.

A residential special school will offer the same kind of facilities and, in addition, will provide a highly organised leisure programme in which a child may be helped to live and cope with others. A major benefit for many who attend these schools is that, away from the emotional demands of the family, they are able to focus on their schoolwork and to experience success in relationships. Meanwhile, their families are given respite and so are more able to manage the child when he returns home. Consider the possible benefits of a residential placement for your child and yourself, together. It is important that your child looks positively upon whatever arrangement is made and does not feel that you are rejecting him.

If your child has a serious disorder, and especially if medication is to be part of the treatment programme, he may be placed in a small school attached to a hospital where his behaviour can be carefully monitored.

There is a wide range of special schools and facilities scattered throughout the country. They provide many different kinds of setting for a wide range of childhood disorders. Again, you can get information and advice from your local library and other specialist associations (see Appendix A).

Respite

Whatever your situation, you will need to recruit help if you are going to have either more time for yourself and the rest of your family or more time for your child. Friends, relatives and neighbours will undoubtedly be aware of your child's difficult behaviour, and you may feel that they would be unwilling to become involved. But the fact is that they may not know of the reasons for his behaviour, and if you explain to them the nature of his problems and how you feel about the situation, you may find that they will take a more sympathetic attitude and be willing to help.

Rather than be defensive about your child's behaviour and by doing so lose the support of your neighbours, friends and relatives, you would do better to share your concerns with them. If you explain the stress to which your child is subjecting you and the rest of your family, they may well listen and understand. Your child needs people other than yourself to whom he can relate. He needs someone who is less attached to him, another relationship that is qualitatively different. You will find that if he has this other person to relate to, he will often behave completely differently with him or her. His attitude to you will also change. It is often the case that if a child is given the opportunity of an alternative relationship he will relax in his present one. If you do manage to recruit the help of a neighbour, friend or relative and arrange for your child to visit him or her, you may find that he begins to use this facility when things become too much for him at home. On the other hand, just the awareness that the 'escape valve' exists may ease the pressure he feels—and he may never actually use it.

In some instances, and particularly when he is older, it may be possible for a difficult child to live with someone else and visit his parents when he feels able to do so. Although this may seem a bizarre suggestion, your child might behave so well in this situation that he would be a pleasure for the other person and a delight to you when he returned. Coping with close relatives, and with the consequent emotional demands, is difficult for most of us, but for the more vulnerable child it can exacerbate his problems. By separating—literally—both you and your child might acquire a greater sense of identity and feel strong enough to cope with the demands that you make on each other. Do consider the possibility of arranging regular short-term and longer-term periods of respite with an understanding relative. Alternatively, if your child has been assessed as having a disorder, this kind of facility may be available through the professional agencies that have been involved with him; some charitable organisations see this as their primary purpose (see Appendix A).

CONSIDER YOURSELF

Become more assertive

Earlier, I stressed the importance of being separate from your child and remaining in a position where you can be a source of strength for him. Because of his personal problems a difficult child will often embroil his parents in his style of behaviour, and you can soon lose sight of who you are and be unable to provide him with the guidance and sense of security that he so badly needs.

You may well be a healthily assertive parent, but if you feel that you are not, the following advice may help.

Assess what you mean to him (or to anyone else):

1 What do you do in your spare time?
2 What are your political views?
3 What is your main ambition in life?

Take action:

1 Make sure that you have an interest in something. Take a night class; join a society. If you can't afford to do this, you can still have a hobby. Walking is good for you, and a well respected activity; and gardening and bird-watching are popular. Research your interest free of charge at your library. While you are there,

look on the notice board—you may find that a group of enthusiasts meets near you.

Pondering on things in your armchair in front of the television is not good enough. Children do not respect couch potatoes. You must *do something*. Physical exercise is extremely good for you, since it will strengthen you not just physically but psychologically. You might also consider attending your local church. Although you may not think of yourself as a believer, it could be a way of becoming involved in good works and meeting new people. It could also provide you with a network of support and promote an inner calm within you. If you like the idea of doing good works—thinking a little more of others rather than dwelling all the time on your own problems—but feel that it would be hypocritical to go to church, you could find details of local voluntary groups in your library or at the Citizens' Advice Bureau.

2 You must have views on the current political scene. If you don't already, start by buying a national newspaper and looking at current issues; use the library to become better acquainted with popular topics. And don't keep your views to yourself; practise stating your opinion, but do still listen to others. You may find that if you let your views be known it will bring you friends who have similar interests.

3 You must have dreams and aspirations. You may be like many people and never have told others what they are. Try discussing them light-heartedly, and try sharing with others your fears and apprehensions—it is by doing this that you will become close to them.

It is important that you mean something to those around you, that in their eyes you stand for something. If you can achieve this, your child too will begin to see you in a positive way—but, more importantly, you will begin to think differently about yourself. You will become a person in your own right, with your own interests and convictions. You will be separate from your difficult child and appear to him as a source of strength rather than weakness.

Become more in tune with your child

Although it is important for you to be strong for your child, you still need to understand and empathise with his thoughts and feelings—and to spend time with him. You may well be offering him the right blend of warmth and firmness. But if you suspect you may not be, it is worth considering whether you are too removed, too 'distanced', from him to provide the necessary support, or whether your own strong interests work against his.

Assess the time you spend with him and how much you know of his thoughts and feelings:

1 How much time have you spent just with him in the last week?
2 Can you describe his thoughts about any current family, local or national/international events? Can you say how he has expressed his feelings about something—in his words, not yours?

Take action:

1 You may presently do all you can to avoid spending time with your difficult child—but if you are to develop a meaningful relationship with him, one that will promote a positive response when you ask him to do something, you should make every effort to allocate a special time just for him. You may find this difficult, but to begin with you could make it a very limited session—say ten minutes—and gradually extend it. If he is already doing something, quietly join in. If you feel that he might be open to a suggestion, ask him whether he could help you in a household chore. Whatever you chose to do, tread carefully, and if necessary just sit in the background and listen. Sharing enjoyable experiences with your child is essential if you want him to respond to you, but this does not mean doing anything special or spending money. Just being together and focusing on helping him to express his thoughts and feelings will be enough.

Choose a time and place for your session that offers the least potential for problems. The last thing you want, especially in the initial stages, is to make your child feel that you are criticising him. Don't expect him to respond immediately. The process may take a very long time, but if you persist and the sessions become part of his routine they will become powerful motivators for him.

2 As your sessions progress, continue to focus on listening to your child and gently encouraging him to express his thoughts about what is happening either at school or in the locality. If he has a particular enthusiasm, or even if he seems only to be interested in television, use it as the basis for helping him to express his thoughts and to be open about his feelings. When it is appropriate, begin to reciprocate by expressing your own views and saying how you feel about certain issues, bearing in mind at all times that the purpose is still not to promote your views but to improve your child's self-esteem. If you are a person with strong personal interests and opinions you will need to be wary of imposing them on him and to be careful not to judge him according to how enthused he is with your interests, how capable of taking part, or how far he agrees with your opinions.

In essence, you should be asking yourself whether you have got the balance right between having strong personal interests of your own and making time to spend with your child.

* * *

In Chapter 9 we shall be looking in more detail at forms of treatment that specialists may recommend for specific disorders. Now, we shall examine some basic principles of practice that have been found to be effective with children who present a variety of behavioural problems. As we do this, we shall again touch on some of the topics that may crop up in your discussions with your child's teacher, with the family doctor or with any specialist that you may be referred to. In other words, we shall be taking a final check that you are doing all *you* can to help alleviate the situation.

GENERAL PRINCIPLES

Meeting his basic psychological needs

We all have certain basic psychological needs if we are to avoid problems, and it is worth considering whether you are meeting those of your child. Take your time in reading these, and after each one ask yourself:

- How far am I meeting this need?
- What can I do about it?

1 The need to have a clear picture of his world

A child needs to feel that he has certain people in his life who will always be there; certain events must always occur; certain rules must always apply. He must know where he stands in relation to everything around him. He needs a map of his personal world—one that can be recognised, one where the compass points do not change.

2 The need to have an objective in life

A child needs to have a level of expectation to work to. He needs to know that there are certain rules that are beyond him, that cannot be questioned. He needs to sense that there are certain objectives for him to achieve—these objectives need to be in the interests of others, not just in his own.

3 The need to feel part of things

He needs a sense of relatedness. He needs to be able to see himself as part of a whole. He needs to sense that he is of value to others, that he is part of a network that gives him a sense of his identity. He needs to belong.

4 The need for stimulation

He needs stimulation. This will help him to develop language and a capacity for abstract thought. It will also help him to develop his inner controls. Severe boredom can lead to severe problems; children have been known to mutilate themselves or even kill others in an attempt to feel a sense of their existence.

5 The need for a sense of rootedness

A child needs to bond with his mother. This happens in the very early stages of childhood and provides an anchor point for future development. With this foundation he can become a separate person with a sense of independence, free will and control. If the bonding does not take place with his mother or another significant person, he may later attempt to form a similar relationship with others and either try to control them (sadism) or be controlled by them (masochism). He may become excessively fond of himself, or have a craving to destroy.

6 *The need for love*

The sense of love, of unconditional acceptance, is built into the bonding process with a child's mother; we also believe that it can be achieved in a slightly different form with others. Unconditional acceptance is not the only necessary component: it is just as important to recognise that love means caring, and that caring means trying to satisfy all the needs that I have already mentioned.

To summarise—are you offering your child:

1 consistency?
2 a sense of purpose?
3 a sense of belonging?
4 stimulation?
5 a sense of achievement?
6 an underlying sense of being cared for and accepted?

Strengthening him

When you are unsure about the precise nature of your child's behavioural problems, an effective way of coping is to think of him as being emotionally fragile. You may feel that your awkward, belligerent child is anything but fragile, but if you can accept the theory then you will undoubtedly be able to deal with him in a more positive and effective way.

When we are born, we are endowed with varying degrees of intelligence and a wide range of physical attributes. We are also born with our own unique emotional quotient. While some of us find it hard to cope with stressful circumstances and could be described as fragile, others can cope well because of their natural resilience. Most people are somewhere in between and are usually able to react to events in a balanced way that does not impair their lives. But a person who is particularly vulnerable may find it hard to cope and will react defensively as he tries to protect himself. If your child is emotionally fragile he will either withdraw into his own world for safety or strike out, either verbally or physically, at those around him. He is feeling vulnerable and trying to protect himself.

We all employ defence mechanisms:

- If we do something wrong, we blame it on others. When good things happen we try to take credit for them. We can never do anything wrong.
- We exaggerate the part that we play in shaping the events in which we have participated. We hype our own performance.
- We invent personal handicaps, before the event, in order to avoid failure. In other words, the excuses come before the event as a guarantee of safety.
- If we feel threatened we may counterattack with verbal aggression or sarcasm, twist information to suit our purpose or avoid what we do not want to hear.

When you are thinking about your child's behaviour, estimate how far he employs these defence mechanisms. When you are assessing how you cope with him, remember that they are an indication of his fragility. If you do this, your purpose will become clear: you are there to strengthen him, to improve his self-esteem. So a useful question to ask yourself is: When he behaves defensively, do I condemn and reject him, or do I make him feel better about himself?

Communicating with him

A great many behavioural problems may be avoided if you communicate effectively with your child. Again, thinking of him as being emotionally vulnerable will help. If he is particularly fragile he will react with an outburst

- if he cannot get what he wants
- if he feels criticised
- if he feels that a situation is unfair.

You can often prevent an angry reaction in these situations by taking time to explain things to him and by expressing yourself clearly.

Speaking to him

- If you speak to him when he is calm, he is more likely to receive your message.
- If you speak slowly and in a non-threatening but confident manner, you will make him feel secure.

- If you repeat the message in a number of ways, it will have a greater chance of filtering through his high level of anxiety.
- Remember his low self-esteem and always speak to him in private.

Encourage him to express himself

It is difficult for many people to express themselves, and for no one more than the child who is particularly vulnerable. He needs you to help him crystallise his thoughts; this is a necessary part of the formation of his identity. He may find it easier to express himself in non-verbal ways to begin with, so you should provide facilities for this. Drawing, modelling, acting or computing may be more appropriate ways for him to express his feelings, especially if he has few literacy skills. In every home, no matter what the child's age, there should be such materials and equipment for him to use. No matter what his age, this kind of activity is vital to him. It enables him to get in touch with himself, and thereafter with others. From these activities you may lead him into verbal interactions. During activity sessions, whether he is a five-year-old doing his clay modelling or a teenager on his computer, begin to talk to him about what he is doing. This will be his first step towards being able to articulate his feelings and thereafter to become more in control of himself. Doing things is far more effective than simply trying to talk. Also, if a child becomes keen on an activity it will form the basis of meaningful relationships with others, with whom he will communicate. If you give priority to spending time with your child and to expressing an interest in what he is doing, you will find that he will respond more appropriately when you need to discipline him.

Listen to him

A vulnerable child may appear to have no difficulty in expressing himself. Indeed, during an outburst it may seem that his vocabulary is quite extensive! But you should try to remain calm and listen carefully to what he is really saying. Although you may be devastated by his language, you should interpret it as a sign of inner weakness and try to feel out the subtext of what he is saying. In general terms he will usually be expressing his fragility and a sense of frustration.

If you remain calm, take him somewhere private and let him settle down, he may begin to tell you what is upsetting him.

Focus on listening to him, and be wary of saying too much. Allow him time to express himself, and, with your gentle assistance, to reach his own decisions.

Don't be tempted to prod and probe too much; be wary of putting words into his mouth; don't start to tell him what he should by now have learnt from the past or go on about how he should alter his behaviour in the future. Provide a sympathetic ear only. A great deal of harm is done by parents and professionals who promote introspection. Children should be living their lives, not talking about them. When it comes to looking at their past, they must be allowed to do so at their own pace. Your child has to feel his way into an understanding of himself, and you must appreciate that as an adult you will be capable of recognising feelings and dynamics that he cannot. If you project these on to him you will be doing him a great deal of harm—he will adopt psychological and behavioural models in his mind that will have no basis in his intellect or his emotions.

If he feels more able to talk to someone who is not as close to him as you are, don't be disappointed. He may find it difficult to talk to you because, paradoxically, he is *too* close. Talking to someone from whom he is more detached—and with whom he is less emotionally involved—is easier. If (unknown to him) you can arrange this, with a favourite relative of his or a youth club leader or teacher, for instance, it may help him considerably.

Helping him to negotiate

A great many behavioural difficulties arise because a child has little skill in negotiating with others. A fragile child, in particular, will react defensively and create more enemies than friends as he attempts to get what he wants. He needs to be helped to develop his skills. You can tackle this in the following way:

1 *Pinpoint the precise situation that is causing a problem*—e.g., mealtimes.
2 *Analyse his behaviour*—e.g., when he wants things.
3 *List the specific skills that you would like him to learn*—e.g., to do with wanting things at mealtimes, which involves:

(a) getting a place to sit
(b) reaching a compromise when it comes to deciding what to eat

(c) acquiring items on the table
(d) wanting attention: taking into account the needs of others
(e) leaving the table.

4 *Choose a skill and teach it:*

(a) Explain Select one of the behaviours, e.g., deciding what he's going to eat. Choose a time when he is calm and away from others, and explain precisely how he should set about doing it. Don't become emotionally involved and don't admonish him. Treat the matter as similar to teaching etiquette: he needs to know precisely what to do and what to say. Don't threaten him with punishment if he fails to implement your suggestions.
(b) Demonstrate If necessary, demonstrate the behaviour or skill to him in private. If you have appropriate material in storybooks or on video you could use it as a basis for your approach, especially if one of his heroes is involved. If he has a hero on hand, such as one of his friends, and his friend is a good role model, this would be even better.
(c) Rehearse Rehearse the skill with him in private. Avoid telling him what not to do: he may well use such knowledge to great effect! Concentrate on a simple explanation of the sequence of actions and words.

5 *Put the skill into practice* Tell him precisely when you will be expecting him to utilise this skill. For example, rather than leaving him with a vague directive, limit the new behaviour to a specific mealtime such as breakfast. Weigh up whether or not it would be a good idea for you to be present when he first tries it out. A great deal depends on your relationship with him—and on his age. A vulnerable child, or one who is older, will often behave completely differently out of sight of someone who is emotionally involved with him.

Allow him to learn from his experience with the new behaviour, and don't place too much emphasis on the importance of his success. (He may use it against you.) Simply teach him the skill in private and allow him to use it in public. Ask others to quietly observe him.

6 *Keep it fresh* Focus on this skill for no more than a week. During this time give as much reinforcement as is appropriate, but if the behaviour is not implemented put it at the bottom of

your list and move on to the next one. Begin to teach this skill just as you taught the first. In this way you can rotate the skills to be learnt.

Being consistent

Children with behavioural problems often come from families where there are no clear and consistent rules, where the lines of communication are blurred. When matters are discussed they are discussed negatively, and no clear decisions are made. This may be because there is no one person in the family who feels strong enough to take responsibility. Problems can arise when the child receives contradictory messages from parents who disagree, or when another over-involved relative continually makes conflicting decisions. Grandparents, for example, who may regularly be asked to look after the child by his exhausted parents, may see him in a different light and, full of good intentions, make decisions that cause friction between all concerned.

Children need to have a clear picture of family rules, and for this to happen the rules must be consistently applied. Markedly different interpretations between those who care for them will only create confusion. The child who is already experiencing personal difficulties will be particularly sensitive to a lack of consistency.

If you want to prevent confusion, agree on a set of guidelines with those who are involved in looking after the child. Rules can be formulated on such matters as bedtimes, the amount of time to be spent watching TV, and who is to do which household chores. You can also make general procedural rules so as to prevent the child receiving conflicting messages. For example, you could agree that if he is given a decision by one of the adults that decision is never questioned in front of him; that if there is disagreement, it is discussed afterwards, and privately, between the adults. You could also agree that there will be one person who will become the decision-maker; that he or she will apply all the agreed rules and consult the others only before taking major decisions.

A child may also need extra help in appreciating the rules and procedures of the classroom. If he has an attention disorder he may find it hard to remember them, and he will benefit if they are displayed on the walls and regularly explained. His teacher may also need to demonstrate and rehearse procedures, as well as reinforcing success with meaningful rewards.

A key to success is to recognise the importance of communicating effectively with each other. If you are having difficulty with the child, speak to the others who deal with him and decide on a course of action. In this way you will be able to avoid inconsistency and provide him with a sense of certainty and, consequently, of security.

Controlling him

If a child is to feel secure he needs to know that there is somebody, apart from himself, who is in charge of his life.

Maintain the generation gap

Both parents and professionals should recognise the need for a generation gap. They should not try to relate to children by behaving on their level. Children need them as adults who have a different—and, hopefully, more mature—approach to life. They have expectations of parents and teachers, and they disrespect them if these are not fulfilled. They want parents to play with them and share experiences, but expect them to have a different set of values and to remain in a position of control.

Rewards

If you want to alter the behaviour of your child you should, whenever possible, think more in terms of rewarding *good* behaviour than punishing bad. Giving him a reward when he is least expecting it can be very effective. It is not necessary to always explain why you are rewarding him—if you do, he may start to treat it as a game. Neither do your rewards have to be impressive or expensive. A positive comment or a smile at the right time can be a very effective reinforcer.

Punishment (see p. 168)

Nonetheless, the option to punish has to be part of the programme. You may have discussed your child's behaviour with him many times. You may have explained, demonstrated and rehearsed how you would like him to behave—all to no effect. Information seems to go in one ear and out of the other. If he does as you say one moment, when the same situation occurs ten minutes later he has seemingly decided to ignore your instructions.

You need to recognise that his behaviour will not alter unless he has felt the consequences of his unacceptable actions. You may shout at him for ever, and all you will be doing is teaching him how to shout. But if you have the strength to quietly take action, you will help him to become calm and controlled. Remember the old saying, 'Actions speak louder than words.' Make a list of consequences—sanctions and punishments—that you know will be effective. And when he refuses to conform, apply one of them. Explain briefly what you are doing—but don't enter into discussion with him. (Once he knows that the matter is open to negotiation, you will have lost control.) A quiet but firm approach will assure him of your strength.

Suitable consequences could include the cancellation of an anticipated treat, extra chores around the house, an early bedtime or the withdrawal of small privileges that he usually enjoys.

Share time with him (see Become More in Tune with Your Child, p. 127)

Before this approach can be effective you must be in a position where you are offering the child a great deal. If your relationship is barren because you never do anything together—except argue—he will not respond. To remedy the situation, you could begin by expressing casual interest in something that he is doing—it could be something as ordinary as watching a TV programme. Later you might ask if you could join him in a computer game. You don't have to go on expensive outings: your child only needs to sense that you are investing something of yourself before he will conform to your requirements.

Providing him with a structure

Earlier in the chapter we discussed children's needs. An effective way of promoting a sense of purpose, belonging and achievement is to ensure that your child's life has some structure to it. Each day, therefore, should be carefully planned with regular routines, and there should be scheduled events that occur at certain times throughout the week, month and year. Part of this structure could be provided by ensuring that he regularly attends a local club or society, or that he is allowed friends home on a particular day of the week. If your lifestyle is chaotic your vulnerable child will suffer. As I mentioned earlier, he needs a predictable, unchanging schedule. If he is provided with this firm platform it will allow him to cope with change when he is ready to do so.

Providing him with an escape route (see Respite, p. 125)
If it is at all possible you should provide your child with his own room. If this is equipped with things for him to do he will be able to use it whenever he feels unable to cope with other people. In this way he will not be kept in a situation that may only lead to failure for him. He will be able to regulate his own behaviour.

Focus on his room being not a place where he is sent as a punishment, but somewhere he can go without shame, to be on his own. Remember that the vulnerable child has difficulty in relating to others. He needs his own space.

Helping him to make friends
If your child has personal problems this will undoubtedly be reflected in his difficulties in making and sustaining friendships. But as we have noted previously, if he is to withstand the pressures around him he will need others in whom he can confide.

Most friendships develop through shared interests. You could therefore help him to make friends by encouraging him to join local clubs or societies. When you are choosing an organisation make sure that it will provide him with a clear structure within which he can feel safe, and which will in this way allow for his initial difficulties. Make sure also that it is an organisation that does not focus primarily on providing opportunities to make friends but has a strong specialist interest. If your child can become enthusiastic about the activities of the organisation, he will find that friendships begin to develop, whereas if you emphasise that he is attending in order to make friends, the opposite will happen. If necessary, meet the leader beforehand and explain your child's difficulties—but do make sure that he understands the importance of not overplaying them.

You can also invite some of his peers to your home. In preparation for the visit, ensure that there are a number of things for them to do, but don't direct their play. Include the possibility of your child being able, if he wants to, to withdraw for a while into his own room—if the others are playing nearby, it will still be a start. In this way he will be able to monitor his behaviour and withdraw when he knows that he is not coping. If you keep the sessions short and provide initial background supervision, you may with patience have some success. If you need to intervene, make sure that you do so by pretending that something or other needs to be done—never criticise your child, or his friends, when they are all present.

In the event of a 'crisis', casually deflect the children into one of the alternative activities that you have thought of beforehand.

Helping him through exercise

The value of regular, disciplined exercise cannot be overestimated, and for no child more than for the one suffering from inner personal problems. So introduce him to pleasurable physical exercise at an early age; as he grows older, regular exercise should become part of his daily routine.

Never:

- force him to take part in team games
- deride his physical ineptitude
- project the idea that for him to be a 'success' he has to have sporting ability.

Always:

- focus on his personal fitness
- carefully assess his abilities
- select activities for their capacity to promote:

1 a sense of achievement
2 sustained interest
3 support from others.

Exercises

To promote personal confidence in your child, encourage him to perform in private a schedule of regular, daily exercises. Give him achievement targets that are just beyond his reach, but that he will be able to achieve within an allotted period of time. His full exercise schedule should be made up of three elements:

1 repetition exercises, with clearly defined targets
2 running or swimming, with clearly defined targets
3 recreational games, such as squash or table tennis, with yourself or another adult who has some knowledge of the games being played.

As with other things that I have recommended, it will be important for either you or an enthusiastic 'coach' to take part—at least initially. If you don't, you will be unable to estimate suitability—or unsuitability—of the programme and your child's enthusiasm may soon disappear.

Group activities

When you feel that he is ready, arrange for him to take part in a group sport. He may need your presence and support at first, but if he can become involved with a group of enthusiasts he will benefit enormously from the network of support that they may provide. He may become a very good sportsman or simply a committed club member. In either case, he will become physically fit and as a consequence feel better about himself.

Seriously consider encouraging him to join a martial arts club. A central aim of such associations is to develop a person's self-control through disciplined physical routines. Some focus more on this aspect than others: T'ai Chi Ch'uan, for example, can be extremely useful as a discipline for promoting both physical fitness and personal congruence. Any exercise, such as yoga or gymnastics, that involves an element of self-discipline could help him to relax and improve his self-esteem.

Providing opportunities for spiritual support

Even if you yourself are an unbeliever, bear in mind that religion could help your child a great deal. Because he is often unable to cope with both himself and the circumstances around him he, more than most, needs someone who will always be there for him. Daily prayer may serve the purpose of focusing him on something outside himself and be a source of strength; it may provide him with an opportunity to crystallise his thoughts and feelings at the end of each day. Attending church on a Sunday may prove a trial to begin with, but it could provide him with a genuine network of support—it might even prove to be a lifeline for him in the future.

CONCLUSION

You may have been reluctant to consider the possibility that your child has a disorder, perhaps because you thought that this would automatically involve psychiatric attention and medication. But in all instances, before recommending medication, a specialist would carefully consider whether your child might be helped by making adjustments at home and at school. Even if medication *is* prescribed—and this is far from being the automatic response—you will still be expected to provide the optimum setting for it to work. As we have seen in this chapter, there are many things that can be done at home in order to ease the situation—and no doubt any specialist that your child might be referred to would be able to recommend many more strategies that would be particularly appropriate for him or her.

We shall now look at some of the ways in which problems can be minimised when he or she is at school.

8 At School

So far we have considered the difficult child's problems principally from the home perspective. We shall now look at some general teaching approaches and techniques that have been found to be useful with children exhibiting a wide range of behavioural disorders. Techniques for specific problems would, of course, be suggested by your Special Educational Needs Coordinator or by the specialists who may become involved, and form part of the child's Individual Education Plan (a brief summary of examples can be found in Chapter 9).

YOUR APPROACH

Although you may be fully committed to working with difficult children, it is worth beginning by reassessing your general approach. For a start, if your school is to provide a consistent setting for the difficult child you may need to persuade your more academic colleagues to consider the following issues.

The focus of your work

1 *Is the primary focus of your work the imparting of knowledge and information—e.g., teaching your subject specialism?*
If it is, you may be promoting difficulties with the more vulnerable child. So adopt a mental stance in which the conveying of information and skills becomes a bonus: if you do, you will be less frustrated and it will be considerably easier to motivate all your pupils—not only those with special needs.

Focus on each child's need for recognition; greet her as she enters the room; take an interest in her as a person.

(2) *Do you focus on the possibility of a child having learning difficulties and emotional problems?*
If you are focusing on the difficulties that children *may* be having,

you will be minimising the possibility of disruptive behaviour. If you see your role as observing behaviour, then linking it to learning, you will be in a better position to promote a child's self-esteem. Read the subtext of her behaviour.

3 *Are you aware of how a difficult child might be reflecting your behaviour?*

If you are agitated and out of control, if you are loud and bullying, or if your style is autocratic, you will breed the same kind of attitude in your pupils. But if you are calm and do not panic you can be a tower of strength to those around you. Whether you are aware of it or not, children will model themselves on you.

Ten principles of practice

It may help to check your approach against the following strongly recommended principles of practice which can be profitably employed by both the home and the school when they are dealing with a child who is displaying any kind of behavioural difficulty:

1 Parents and teachers work together.

They must:

2 anticipate the problems the child may have
3 repeat instructions
4 praise her frequently
5 focus on rewards
6 use immediate, frequent and appropriate consequences (see Positive Reinforcement, p. 167 and Punishment, p. 168)
7 display rules
8 break tasks down into manageable portions—focus on the possibility of success
9 provide escape routes, such as quiet areas
10 maintain a good level of stimulation—provide a range of alternative activities.

Emphasis must be placed on:

- predictable schedules
- clear boundaries
- clear expectations.

PRACTICAL TIPS

New entries

Make every effort to find out about any potential problems before a child enters your class. Only by doing this will you be able to plan ahead and avoid the possibility of a poor start with her.

A child who is experiencing problems will find it hard to enter a new class; if you are fully informed about her difficulties you will be able to avoid her 'letting herself down'. Never adopt the dangerous approach of saying that you like to accept a child as she is, and not prejudge her. While she will indeed sense it if you have negative expectations, you nevertheless need to know as much as you can about her background. If you are unaware that she is still in a state of mourning for her deceased father you may cause her great distress by an innocent comment about death; if your well intentioned but ill timed criticism makes an impulsive child feel seriously deficient, you may place yourself and others at risk from her.

Physical safety

Your first duty to the difficult child is to ensure that she is physically safe. Her behaviour may mean that she will be at greater risk than others of having an accident. Always do a risk assessment, even if you are not teaching a practical subject (refer to your school's Health and Safety Policy Document for help). A child who has personal problems may be unpredictable, so you should take all necessary measures to provide the safest possible environment. Lock away dangerous objects such as scissors; when they are needed, be very conscious of their use; when you finish the lesson, monitor their collection.

Never hesitate to express your concerns to the headteacher if you are unhappy with the level of care you are able to provide. Admitting your inability to cope with a difficult child is the first step towards achieving some kind of positive resolution; not to do so could be construed as negligence in the event of an inquiry into a serious incident.

Keeping records, monitoring

If you are to acquire help for the difficult child you will need to provide evidence of her behaviour. Make sure that you record any incidents, however insignificant they may seem, and that you consult others on every occasion. If you record incidents in detail, indicating what happened immediately beforehand (the Antecedents), the Behaviour itself and what happened afterwards (the Consequences), it may be possible to devise useful strategies. Record your assessment of how these have worked, and if you need to refer to the SENCO or to a specialist use them as your points of reference.

If you are pursuing a special behavioural programme with the child, keep records of how she responds, and if she is receiving medication ensure that you carefully monitor the effect that this may be having on her behaviour. Records will also be essential if you are to devise an appropriate Individual Education Plan; in addition, they will be needed for her annual review if she is a child with a Statement of Special Educational Needs.

PEER SUPPORT: WORKING WITH THE GROUP

A vulnerable child may be able to manage quite well on his own—it is often only when he is in the presence of others that his problems are noticed. So it is important to think carefully about the group situation.

Manipulate the group setting

Don't expect the difficult child to relate well to others automatically. Think carefully about how you might arrange your group so as to minimise the possibility of problems occurring. Place her in a position where you or your assistant can provide immediate help and reassurance, and near one of the most mature members of the class. Remember that your aim is to provide her with the safest possible setting—both physical and psychological.

Cultivate group support

You can do this effectively by establishing 'the principle of human variation' in the minds of your group or class. Try to eradicate the notion that all children should be treated the same. All good Special Schools do this—if they didn't, they would soon be unable to operate. If you stress that each child has his own difficulties just as each has his own needs, and that all the pupils are there to help each other work towards upholding the group or classroom rules, you should be able to cultivate an ethos of understanding and support. You will then not be faced, as you attempt to meet the special needs of the difficult child, with the often-heard question, 'Why is he allowed to do this when I'm not?'

Introduce the theme of variation and different needs into all your work. Stress the notion in your casual conversations with the group and in formal discussions.

Never tolerate the notion that a difficult child is evil. When you impose sanctions, stress that you are doing so to help her. If you cultivate an atmosphere of positive mutual support, the negative effects of any child behaving badly within the group will be minimised. The other children will find it easier to accept the particularly difficult one: rather than reject her because of her behaviour, they will begin to regard it as something 'separate' that has to be treated. When she behaves badly they will be able to resist reacting to her; if you tell them precisely what to do when a crisis—with any of them—occurs, they will learn to extinguish unwanted behaviour by ignoring it. Furthermore, if you encourage them to pay attention to others when they are behaving well, this will consolidate your strategy.

To avoid exacerbating the condition of the difficult child you must apply this approach with all the children in the group.

But none of this will be possible if you have been unable to cultivate a strong sense of belonging within the whole group. To do this—and to promote strong group controls—you will need to organise outings and other events over and above the usual timetable commitments. This special time spent with your group is essential if you wish to foster the necessary degree of support.

When you organise these extracurricular events, pay special attention to the needs of the difficult child. Don't presume that because she is getting a treat she will behave well. Make sure that you take plenty of helpers and that you inspire them to see the event as a worthwhile challenge. Never exclude the difficult child from the event—if you must, provide her with alternative 'positive' activities, but make sure that other children join in with her. You must do all you can to avoid ostracising her and exacerbating her condition.

Provide opportunities for retreat

Some of the activities that you provide should take place outside the group setting, thereby allowing the difficult child the chance to withdraw in an acceptable way. For this purpose you could hold in reserve activities to do with your weather station, the school litter bins, the flower bed or your small-pet compound, potential 'release valves' for the child who cannot cope in a group. Or you could arrange for your assistant to take her to the local shop, or for an 'emergency' visit to the school secretary or to the headmaster, to help with some task or other. And whenever possible, make sure that another child accompanies her.

Your classroom should be equipped with booths for private study, or contain an area set aside to which the child can retreat. If such a facility is available for all children—and not used as a punishment—there will be no stigma attached and the difficult child in particular may be able to regulate her own behaviour.

Promote paired responsibilities and friendships

Whenever possible, create opportunities for the difficult child to assume a position of responsibility. Don't resent giving her responsibilities; if you find yourself in the frame of mind that holds that she doesn't deserve them, you have regressed into 'battle stations'. Think of the difficult child as one who is disabled. Responsibilities can prove effective crutches for her. If you are worried about the effect on your group, remember that if you have cultivated a group atmosphere that caters for individual needs, you will be able to accord her privileges and status without appearing to reward her for unacceptable behaviour.

Common to all children who are experiencing problems is their wish for a friend. Whenever possible, pair the difficult child with another child for both work and special responsibilities—one who is secure enough within himself to be able to cope with the demands that she may make upon him. A friendship *may* develop—but, if not, at the very least the difficult child will have a role model and the other pupil will have a chance to put his maturity to the test. If you think it's appropriate instruct the difficult child privately, by demonstrating and rehearsing, how to speak to and negotiate with others; in other words, give her tips on how to avoid making enemies (see Assertiveness Training, p. 163).

Promote peer support/mediation

Children will often respond more positively to one of their peers than they will to an adult. If you have cultivated a feeling of loyalty in your group you may feel it appropriate to use either the group or an individual child to support another who is having difficulty.

CONFLICT RESOLUTION

The group, or certain individuals, should be trained in conflict-resolution techniques. In essence, they should be taught that it is important to:

- respect each person's right to their point of view
- try and understand how other people *feel*
- come to a solution without hurting others.

They should also be taught to:

- be good listeners
- make it clear to the child in question that they are listening, by reflecting back what she is saying
- allow everyone a chance to express themselves
- remain impartial
- guide the parties (or individual) concerned towards identifying the problem
- encourage them to formulate a solution that is acceptable to all
- discuss ways of avoiding similar problems in the future.

ANGER MANAGEMENT

If the group are aware of how to manage their anger they will become more tolerant of each other and be in a better position to understand and help the more vulnerable child.

They should be helped to identify:

- *triggers*—
  1. make a list of specific triggers for their anger
  2. work out how they can avoid these triggers

- *thoughts*—
  1. describe what they were thinking, what made them angry, in a specific instance
  2. consider alternative thinking—an alternative interpretation of the episode—that would not have involved anger

- *feelings*—
  1 describe how they feel when they first start to get angry
  2 consider strategies to employ that will help them keep calm

- *appropriate ways of expressing anger*—
  1 wait until they are calm before expressing anger
  2 listen to the other person's view
  3 resist blaming the other person
  4 focus on expressing a solution to the problem
  5 resist getting things out of proportion.

WORKING WITH THE CHILD

Encourage self-monitoring

An effective way of helping a child to cope with her behaviour is to encourage her to monitor it. You could, for example, discuss a particular aspect of her behaviour, then tell her to keep a tally of the number of times it occurs; if she finds this too difficult, you could design a secret system that prompts her to add each instance to her tally. Studies have shown that it is not important whether the tally is correct or not: the mere use of the system can bring about a dramatic decrease in the frequency of unwanted behaviour, as the child becomes more aware of it.

Help her to find solutions

Introduce her to a set of simple questions that she can ask herself:

- *when she is restless*—
  'Where do I feel the restlessness?'
  'What is causing me to feel this way?'
  'Why am I blaming someone else?'
  'Who should I tell about this?'
- *when she is unable to make decisions*—
  'What are my options?'
  'Which is the one I want to take?'
  'Why do I hesitate?'

In this way you might help her to cope with her condition rather than leaving her confused.

Teach her social skills
Focus on the child's inability to cope with others: give her a systematic programme of training in social skills. Don't expect her to automatically know how to behave; she needs to be shown precisely what to do, and to practise in safety. Make a list of her priorities.

Select a specific situation and describe it in detail; privately demonstrate and rehearse the way in which it should be managed (see Assertiveness Training, p. 163).

Teach her to understand others
You could teach basic counselling skills to the difficult child. You might demonstrate and rehearse, through role play, how to listen to someone who is conversing with her, reflect on what the other person says and affirm it. The difficult child is often unaware of the feelings and needs of others. Because of her own inner problems she may misinterpret what they say. To help her, you could provide exercises in which she pauses and silently asks herself what the other person is saying—the subtext of their conversation. In these ways you may help her to develop more meaningful relationships with them (see Counselling, p. 175).

Teach her to control her anger
Whether the child is outwardly aggressive or withdrawn, she is likely to be angry inside. All children would benefit from knowing how to manage their anger (see Anger Management, p. 149).

WORKING WITH OTHERS

You will need a great deal of help if you are to work successfully with a child who is experiencing significant difficulties.

Parents

To be really effective in your work with a difficult child, you need to do all you can to cultivate a relationship with her parents. Studies show that when the parents of difficult children are generally supported—when they feel better about themselves—the behaviour of their children improves dramatically. To achieve this 'feel good' factor, arrange to visit the child's home and chat to the parents—about themselves, not their child. Do this preferably before she enters your class.

Invite the parents into your classroom. Allow the child to show them around the school. Take a genuine interest in them, as people. Remember that whereas you have only to spend your working shift with this child who causes you so many problems, they have to live with her permanently. Imagine the stress and trauma they suffer having to deal with their child on a twenty-four-hour basis. Don't condemn them and lecture them about how to bring her up. Listen to them and ask them about *their* background. Later you may be able to gently suggest techniques that they might employ—but don't preach to them!

If you are able to recruit them as working partners, your chances of succeeding with their child will be considerably enhanced. So as to involve them in dealing with her behaviour, keep them regularly informed about your concerns—perhaps weekly. Don't assume that they are aware of the many daily incidents that are happening at school. If the child is involved in a serious incident, inform them immediately.

You may feel it appropriate to work out together an effective behavioural contract for the child, involving commitment not only from her but from yourself and her parents. The behaviour of all children may improve dramatically if parents are involved in this way. It is generally not advisable, however, for a parent of a difficult child to be directly involved in the classroom—the child's behaviour will inevitably be adversely affected by her presence.

Colleagues

If you can recruit the assistance of your colleagues, the task of dealing with the vulnerable child will become far less onerous. Not only will you feel supported by openly sharing your difficulties, but between you you can devise useful simple strategies. For instance, a system of prompts between teachers and their assistants can be designed to implement the technique of third-party intervention. The third party—another member of staff summoned by the assistant well before the crisis point is reached—can present a fresh approach and effectively deflect the child into an alternative, positive activity. Mutual arrangements can be made with colleagues to provide each other with this facility.

STRATEGY CHECKLIST

Checking your classroom techniques against the following lists may help you to assess more accurately whether you are doing all you can to help the difficult child, and whether you need further specialist advice. Whether you have a large or a small class, if you have a child who is experiencing significant difficulties you will undoubtedly need the services of a *classroom assistant*, who can provide the child not only with practical help but with general reassurance. It will be of great benefit if he or she can be involved in considering the following strategies:

NB In some instances I suggest here some established techniques that may be recommended for use with particular behaviours (brief summaries can be found in Chapter 9). While elements of these techniques may be familiar to you and already built into your repertoire, others must only be used by a trained specialist. Most of the therapies, in particular, are provided for your reference only, unless you have a qualification to use them. In the child's interests and your own, never use any techniques that are not detailed in her Individual Education Plan and approved by your SENCO, head of department or headteacher.

For pupils who find it difficult to concentrate

- Display procedures and rules.
- Examine group dynamics carefully. Before the pupils enter the room, decide where they will sit.
- Place particularly difficult pupils near good role models.
- Space them away from each other, according to need.
- Seat them away from any distractions, *but*
  —provide a range of powerful stimuli to which they can be deflected when their attention fades.
- Provide private areas to enable self-regulating to take place—and have more than one of these, to avoid giving the impression of discrimination.
- Provide assignments to suit the length of individual concentration spans; acknowledge the completion of tasks immediately, and reward if appropriate.
- Break long assignments into small parts.

- Provide a clear outline of the lesson or activity at the beginning. Recap at the end.
- Recap regularly; use the difficult pupil's good work or good performance to illustrate points; repeat and reinforce throughout the lesson or activity.
- Have a variety of activities available for the session.

For pupils who are unable to organise and plan

- Establish routines and schedules for each day, lesson or activity.
- Display schedules whenever possible, and explain them repeatedly.
- Establish clear requirements for the presentation of work.
- Constantly monitor work for neatness.
- Write up the main points on the board whenever you are explaining anything.
- Demonstrate and rehearse requirements—privately.
- Provide simple written study guides for homework topics.
- Give practice in dividing assignments into short stages.
- Encourage pupils to keep a daily diary.

For pupils who are impulsive

- Have a wide range of alternative activities available.
- Provide a facility for self-regulation—a booth or other quiet area (see also Time Out, p. 173).
- Have clear and simple class rules—explain, demonstrate and rehearse (see Modelling, p. 166).
- Ignore minor behaviour problems (see Extinction, p. 165).
- Provide short tasks.
- Provide short-term behavioural targets.
- Focus on more immediate rewards and consequences (see Positive Reinforcement, p. 167; Token Economy System, p. 173).
- Avoid criticising the difficult pupil when reprimanding her for her actions.
- Provide specific self-monitoring techniques for her, with rewards. For instance, before she speaks in class insist that she puts up her hand and gains permission to do so by eye contact. Arrange this procedure in private beforehand, and reward

privately, also as pre-arranged (see Prompting, p. 168; Shaping, p. 171).

- Teach her to pause before acting, and to think of the consequences (see Cognitive Behaviour Modification, p. 164; Self-instruction Training, p. 180)

For pupils who find it difficult to comply

- Display class rules conspicuously.
- Provide immediate feedback on acceptable and unacceptable behaviour.
- Praise compliant behaviour (see Positive Reinforcement, p. 167); attempt to ignore minor non-compliance (see Extinction, p. 165).
- Encourage the difficult child to think of her behaviour and its consequences (see Contingency Contracting, p. 164; Interpersonal Cognitive Problem-solving, p. 179; Punishment, p. 168).
- Consider the need that she may have to examine the logic behind her behaviour (see Rational Emotive Therapy, p. 177).

For pupils who find it difficult to interact with others

- Monitor their interactions with others.
- Design a social-skills training programme dealing with the specific items of behaviour observed, in order of priority. Demonstrate and rehearse in private (see Assertiveness Training, p. 163).
- Place such pupils in situations where they may learn to interact positively with others.
- Provide responsibilities for the individual pupil.
- Pair her with a good role model on specific projects (see Modelling, p. 166).
- In extreme cases allow a pupil to regulate her own time with the group: provide alternative activities or locations. Take the initiative here, so as to avoid the pupil thinking that nobody is caring for her.
- Consider whether she may benefit from being aware of techniques inherent in Counselling (p. 175) or Transactional Analysis (p. 180).

For pupils who have mood swings or who are anxious

- Provide continual reassurance and encouragement.
- Look for opportunities for the individual pupil to assume responsibilities.
- Focus on her talents and use them to promote a sense of self-worth and identity.
- Consider whether she may benefit from learning how to cope with her reactions (see Stress-inoculation Training, p. 179).
- Consider whether she may benefit from analysing her behaviour (see Rational Emotive Therapy, p. 177; Transactional Analysis, p. 180).
- Consider whether she may benefit from any of the therapies summarised in Chapter 9.

For pupils who have difficulty in communicating

- Focus on providing reassurance and reducing anxiety.
- Focus on experiential learning.
- Provide a variety of alternative ways in which the child may express herself.
- Supplement clear instructions with non-verbal cues (facial and bodily gestures) (see Prompting, p. 168), and encourage the child to use them herself.
- Teach her how to recognise these cues—demonstrate, rehearse, reward (see Modelling, p. 166).
- Provide explicit (literal) instructions rather than posing vague rhetorical questions.
- Avoid similes, metaphors and ambiguous statements, but work towards an appreciation of these.
- Be aware that the child's mode of communication will be modelled on yours.
- Provide short-term targets with rewards for behaviour—e.g., for not interrupting, for not thinking aloud (see Positive Reinforcement, p. 167; Token Economy System, p. 173).
- Teach her specific social communication skills—e.g., turn-taking, maintaining a social distance when talking (see Assertiveness Training, p. 163).
- Teach her how to initiate conversation, maintain it, then terminate it (see Modelling, p. 166).

- Encourage her to appreciate the thoughts and feelings of others through role play.
- Consider whether she may benefit from a modification of the techniques inherent in Stress-inoculation Training (p. 179) or Self-instruction training (p. 180).

For pupils who have learning difficulties

Reading and mathematics

- Note any significant discrepancies between the child's general ability (IQ) and her attainment in literacy.
- Check her hearing and sight and note any 'visual discomfort' she may have (e.g., a need for coloured filters or lenses).
- Administer suitable diagnostic tests as early as possible (consult your SENCO for details of effective computerised tests that teachers can use, or refer the child to an educational psychologist).
- Teach specific skills, and recognise the child's need for overlearning.
- Use a multisensory approach (visual/auditory/kinaesthetic).
- Use a structured, sequential and cumulative approach.
- In reading, focus on phonics; in mathematics, focus on practical work.
- In both reading and mathematics, focus on:
  —working from what the child already knows (see Shaping, p. 171)
  —providing reassurance and reinforcement (see Positive Reinforcement, p. 167; Token Economy System, p. 173)

For pupils who have problems with coordination

- Note the discrepancy between the child's age and both her gross and fine motor skills.
- Check her sight, hearing and speech: estimate any need for specialist assistance.
- Identify the specific problems.
- Provide regular private training sessions for specific skills.

Gross motor skills

- As appropriate, provide exercises that will promote skills related to:
  - —balance and posture
  - —the control of momentum and the ability to change direction
  - —the ability to make slow, precise and controlled movements.
- Focus on the skills of catching, throwing, kicking and batting.
- Use elements from gymnastics to promote a positive and clear body image and spatial awareness.
- Use dance to promote rhythm, sequencing and movement memory.

Fine motor skills

- Check the coordination of the two eyes of the child: refer her to a specialist if necessary.
- *For writing skills*, focus on:
  - —strengthening the fingers through finger games
  - —basic pencil-holding and elementary sequential writing patterns
  - —large-scale writing (kinaesthetic approach) with guidelines, gradually reducing the size
  - —when appropriate, providing alternative ways of recording information.
- *For reading skills* (see Learning Difficulties, p. 157), focus also on:
  - —the need to adjust the size of the text when necessary (consider the use of a magnifier)
  - —the difficulty that the child may have in locating the text (she can use a piece of card)
  - —the need to keep any copying to a minimum (she may have difficulty in locating the information, retaining it and then putting it in the right place).

DEALING WITH CRISES

If you are anxious when teaching a child with behavioural problems, it is probably because you know that at any time she could be at the centre of a major incident of verbal or physical aggression. You may be permanently 'on edge' because of her unpredictability. If you *are* anxious it will undoubtedly affect the child, and to avoid potential problems you should be clear about how to minimise the possibility of a crisis and, equally importantly, about what you will do if one occurs.

General preventative techniques

1 *Avoid unwanted 'incidents'*, and avoid excluding pupils from your session, by:

- thinking of the needs of particularly difficult pupils *before* the session begins
- planning to meet these needs rather than deny them
- having alternative standby strategies, previously arranged with other staff, which will allow you to maintain control (see Colleagues, p. 152).

2 *Avoid outbursts by:*

- starting the session with a clear explanation of what you will be doing
- never publicly criticising a pupil
- being consistent in your application of rules and procedures, with the proviso that you determine what each individual child needs at any given moment.

3 *Avoid disempowering yourself by:*

- taking the initiative at all times—before the crisis situation has been reached and the child has assumed control
- speaking quietly and firmly without threatening or cajoling, and in the event of this having no effect:
  —taking some form of action with the group rather than continually repeating yourself
- never speaking about difficulties you are experiencing with a group when they are present
- never discussing strategies with another member of staff in the presence of the group.

4 *Avoid indiscipline and confrontation by:*

- Cultivating group loyalty

—Organise group outings: e.g., special trips and expeditions.
—Organise group projects to help other groups: e.g., local charities.
—Elect a group committee, and hold regular group meetings.

What to do in the event of a crisis

Verbal aggression

- Send for help so as to enable you to:
  —separate the child from the group.
- Wait until she is calm; provide reassurance and encourage her to take deep breaths.
- Tell her that you are going to deal with any other children who were involved, but that first you want to help her.
- Encourage her to describe what she thinks she may have done that was wrong—if nothing else, she will have dealt with the situation wrongly by being verbally aggressive.
- Encourage her to tell you what she should have done.
- Suggest to her (don't *tell* her) how she might have avoided letting herself down.
- Tell her what you are going to do about resolving the situation that led to the outburst.
- Reflect back to her what she has told you about her behaviour.
- Reassure her of her worth by focusing on her good points.
- Re-install her in the group setting.

  Finally:
- Do not react by hurling abuse at her.
- Listen to the subtext of what she is saying.

Physical aggression

Ensure that you have training in the physical handling of children and that you are fully aware of your local education authority's guidelines. A simplified, general approach could be:

- Send for help.
- Remove the child from the group, or vice versa.
- Don't place yourself at physical risk by intervening if you know that you arc incapable of doing so effectively.
- If you do feel able to intervene, remember that your purpose in doing so is to:

—prevent the child from harming herself
—prevent her from harming others
—prevent her from damaging property.

- Remember also that:
  —you are allowed to restrain her for these purposes
  —you should use *reasonable* force at all times
  —your intention should be to avoid injury to the child
  —you are not allowed to attack her in any way.
- Don't forget the *five Rs*:
  —Restrain—using authorised holds.
  —Reassure—calm her with reassuring words, while still holding her.
  —Release—gradually, and when her breathing begins to calm.
  —Reinstate—place her back into the group as soon as possible.
  —Recap—privately, and at a later time.

CONCLUSION

Although children present a range of behavioural problems, the strategies and techniques that we have discussed in this chapter have been found to work well across the board. Most of them can be used by non-specialists and many of their inherent principles form the basis for any kind of effective teaching. But other, special, techniques may be available for particular behavioural disorders, and for these you will need to seek further advice through your SENCO. The fact that most children who are having difficulty exhibit the symptoms of more than one disorder means that someone is going to have to sort out priorities, and for this you will need specialist help. The most important thing you can do as a teacher is to make sure that you identify problems as soon as possible.

Many difficulties can be considerably alleviated by using simple strategies, and these are most effective if employed in the early stages and consistently applied by all concerned.

9 Treatment Techniques

When a specialist has diagnosed your child's problems she may recommend one or more of a wide range of treatment approaches. Treatment is as complex as diagnosis, and discovering the best combination of techniques will take time. The problems that each child presents are unique, and while a specialist will have a good idea of a formula for success, she can guarantee nothing. It is important to appreciate this and not to expect that once you have got an appointment your problems are over. In reality, you will have only just begun to explore possibilities, and it would be unrealistic to expect any quick-fix instant solution.

Whether you are a parent or a teacher, you will avoid a great deal of frustration if you think of yourself as part of a team of adults who, by trial and error, are going to come to the best possible combination of treatment approaches for the child. Focusing on helping him to cope with his condition, rather than expecting a 'cure', will also help.

The forms of treatment available are as varied and numerous as the disorders themselves. In Chapters 7 and 8 we have already discussed many strategies that you can employ, and explained the principles of such techniques as peer mediation, conflict resolution and anger management. In this chapter we shall take a brief look at some of the many other techniques that may be recommended.

Caution These very basic, simplified summaries are for general background information only. You are strongly advised not to use them unless you have already been advised to do so by your child's specialist, and instructed in greater detail by her. As with any other form of treatment, they may prove extremely harmful if administered inappropriately. Although you may recognise, and indeed already use, some of the techniques in your own way, bear in mind that your child's behaviour is most likely to be rooted in a number of *co-morbid* (coexisting) disorders. Only a specialist will be able to determine priorities and provide you with the safest and most effective combination of treatment approaches.

BEHAVIOURAL METHODS

Assertiveness training

Aim

- To promote the child's ability to express his thoughts and emotions, freely and appropriately.
- To promote his ability to negotiate without being offended or causing offence.
- To enable him to become more active, confident and involved with others.

Method

Role-play is enacted between child and adult in specific problematic situations (e.g., in expressing thoughts and feelings, or in getting something:

1 Adult discusses the interpersonal situations that cause the child difficulty.
2 She acts the part of the other person.
3 Child and adult reverse roles, with the adult reflecting back the child's responses to him.
4 Adult encourages child to think of his style of relating.
5 She demonstrates the correct way to behave.
6 Child practises the new way of behaving.
7 Adult rewards child for his successful attempt.
8 The process is repeated for other specific scenarios.

Notes

- Specific situations are addressed.
- Prompts are given, as necessary.
- Frequent demonstrations and rehearsal are included.
- Frequent praise and reward are offered.
- Real-life opportunities for practice are provided.

Cognitive behaviour modification

Aim

- To minimise the confusion in the child and to promote his inner control of thoughts and actions.

Method
The adult performs the problematic behaviour, as it *should* be performed, in the presence of the child, and as she does so she talks herself through it. The child is encouraged to do likewise, until he can perform the task silently, with 'internal speech' control:

1. The problem behaviour is chosen.
2. Adult performs the task and talks through her actions in the presence of the child.
3. Child performs the same task and the adult talks him through.
4. He performs the task and talks himself through.
5. He performs the task and whispers himself through.
6. He is told to perform the task using silent 'internal speech'.

Note

- If used with an intellectually disabled child, simple tasks are chosen, with greater repetition.

Contingency contracting

Aim

- To motivate the child towards the desired behaviour, and thereafter build it into his repertoire.

Method
A contract is needed that will clearly describe what behaviour is expected and what will happen if the child does or does not achieve the target, so he and the adult negotiate:

1. a written statement describing in detail the minimum required behaviour (if necessary, adult demonstrates and rehearses the behaviour with the child)
2. the length of the contract and the expected frequency of the acceptable performance

3 a hierarchy of rewards that are meaningful to the child
4 a hierarchy of meaningful penalties
5 bonus rewards that will be available if minimum behavioural expectations are exceeded
6 details of how the performance will be monitored and how feedback will be given to the child.

Notes

- The contract must be negotiated with a willing child and not imposed by the adult.
- The target behaviour must be achievable: if the procedure results in constant failure, it will exacerbate the problem—the child may cheat and experience greater loss of self-esteem.
- The focus is on rewards rather than punishments.
- Both parties must firmly adhere to the contract.
- If the contract fails badly, negotiate a new one, rather than repeat the first.

Extinction

Aim

- To extinguish the child's unacceptable behaviour.

Method
The adult ignores the unacceptable behaviour and reinforces what is acceptable:

1 Adult selects a single, unwanted behaviour.
2 She considers her own reaction to the child's behaviour.
3 When the child's behaviour recurs, she ignores it.
4 Adult pays attention to the child when he is behaving appropriately.

Notes

- The unwanted behaviour may increase initially, before subsiding.
- The child may develop other unwanted behaviours in an attempt to gain attention.

- The adult may need to instruct other adults or siblings to ignore these behaviours.
- The process of change may be slow and prolonged; patient ignoring may be called for.
- Ignoring *must* be accompanied by strong but subtle and consistent reinforcement—attention—whenever the child is behaving appropriately.
- During the ignoring moments the adult should be actively involved in something herself rather than waiting at battle stations.
- If ignoring has to be abandoned because of physical risk to the child, without commenting on his behaviour and without becoming involved emotionally, the adult should remove him to an alternative activity.

Modelling

Aim

- To teach the child a new way of behaving.

Method
The child observes and imitates the behaviour of the adult:

1. The target situation or behaviour is decided upon by adult and child.
2. Child is encouraged to watch the adult as she performs the behaviour appropriately.
3. Adult asks him to describe what he has seen and to try and remember it.
4. Adult asks him to close his eyes, to watch her performing the behaviour and to describe what he is seeing—verbally, or by drawing or writing.
5. She asks the child to copy the behaviour a number of times.
6. She asks him to perform the behaviour in his mind and to describe what he is doing.
7. She repeats the process until he can perform it with confidence.
8. He is rewarded either with praise or with something more tangible.

Notes

- The child will only respond if he respects and likes the person working with him.
- That person should be supportive and project a degree of warmth.
- The child will only respond if he considers that the demonstrated behaviour is exemplary: some preliminary discussion of the appropriateness of the demonstrated behaviour may therefore be necessary.
- The best response may be achieved if the demonstrator is another child of the same age, sex and attitudes, and who is liked and respected by the child being treated.

Positive reinforcement

Aim

- To strengthen and maintain desirable behaviours.

Method
The child's acceptable behaviour is reinforced by social and material rewards (see Notes below):

1 Adult observes child and decides on meaningful rewards (see Notes below).
2 She decides on appropriate rewards for a variety of situations.
3 She decides on the required duration of the acceptable behaviour.
4 She gives the child the rewards immediately after the predetermined duration.
5 She gradually reduces the rewards, and thus the intensity of the reinforcement.
6 She pairs the material rewards with the social ones, and gradually phases out the material ones, with only occasional material reinforcers thereafter.

Notes

- The rewards (reinforcers) are selected from three categories, depending on how it is felt the child will best respond:
  —social rewards: praise, approval, affection, recognition

—material rewards: ticks on a chart, food, drink, toys, sweets
—satisfaction rewards: being allowed to do things—e.g., playing games, going to the cinema, helping others.

- To avoid the procedure developing into a meaningless game, the process is discrete—the child is kept unaware of what is happening.

Prompting

Aim

- To enable the child to respond appropriately to given instructions.

Method
The child's behaviour or response is prompted by verbal or non-verbal cues from the adult. These external prompts are gradually reduced, and he learns how to respond on his own.

1 When the adult wishes the child to do something she will prompt him (see Notes below).
2 The prompts will gradually be phased out.

Notes

- Prompts may take the form of:
  —verbal prompts, where the adult issues clear, unequivocal instructions
  —gestural prompts, where, for example, she points to something or beckons someone
  —physical prompts, where she physically guides the child through the required action.
- A combination of these prompts can be used.
- The frequency of prompts is gradually reduced

Punishment

Aim

- To immediately stop or suppress undesirable behaviour, especially when it places the child or others at risk.

Method

Following an undesirable behaviour, the adult either administers an unpleasant consequence or withdraws a pleasure:

1 Adult clearly and calmly explains the undesirability of the child's behaviour.
2 She clearly and calmly explains the details of the punishment; with older children, a degree of discussion or negotiation may avoid accusations of unfairness.
3 Child makes restitution with adult by fulfilling the requirements.
4 Adult acknowledges this, reaffirms future requirements and reassures child with support.

Notes

- Excessive punishment can cause serious harm.
- Punishment should be used as a last resort.
- Punishment should reflect the seriousness of the behaviour and not the mood of the adult.
- Punishment should never be used on its own: it should be outweighed by an emphasis on rewarding appropriate behaviour.
- The child should be made aware that it is his behaviour that is being rejected, and not him.
- Punishment will lose its effect if used frequently, or if it is prolonged.
- The behaviour that is to be punished must be clearly identified and explained.
- The punishment must be clearly and calmly explained and linked to the undesirable behaviour.
- When the undesirable behaviour occurs, the punishment should be administered as soon as possible.
- Punishments should be 'fair' and consistently administered.

Relaxation training

Aim

- To promote muscle relaxation and a feeling of calmness.

Method

The adult encourages the child to perform deep-breathing exercises, to tense and relax his muscles and to use self-help sentences.

1. Adult asks child to lie in a comfortable position, in a room that is warm and has low lights.
2. Adult asks child to breathe in slowly while she counts to five. The child then breathes out slowly to the same count. As he breathes in he is asked to imagine the air entering his lungs and filling them to capacity. As he breathes out he is encouraged to breathe a sigh of relief. The breathing exercise is repeated a number of times and the adult explains that the child can do this whenever he needs to feel calm.
3. Adult asks child to relax his arms and legs.
4. She works through all the muscles of the body, starting with the hands and arms and upper body, then continuing with the stomach, hips, legs, ankles, feet and toes.
5. She demonstrates how to tense, hold and relax muscles.
6. Child is asked to tense each muscle for a few seconds and then relax it. He is asked to notice the difference and to say how he feels.
7. He is encouraged to think and rehearse sentences that he can say to himself whenever he needs to remain calm.

Note

- The deep-breathing exercises, the tensing and relaxation of muscles and the self-help sentences may be used together or separately—as is felt to be appropriate and according to the age of the child.

Shaping

Aim

- To develop and maintain a required skill.

Method

The adult links what a child can already do to the required behaviour and, in small steps, gradually achieves the target by reinforcing at each stage.

1. Adult decides on the objective to be achieved.
2. She observes the child's behaviour and looks for things that he can do that may link with and lead up to the objective to be achieved.
3. She creates a staged programme, starting with something that the child can do.
4. She arranges everything so that he has the maximum possibility of success.
5. She reinforces the first behaviour with praise, affection, food and so on and assists with verbal and gestural instructions and cues.
6. When the behaviour is well established, she progresses towards the objective by moving on to the next stage.
7. The process is repeated until the objective is achieved and powerfully reinforced.

Notes

- If there is no response at any stage, then the programme is revised, with additional, alternative steps being introduced as necessary.
- The emphasis is on powerful rewards.
- As the child achieves each stage, and to maintain the potency of the exercise, the reinforcers become less predictable.

Systematic desensitisation

Aim

- To reduce or eliminate a fear (phobia) or anxiety.

Method

While in a relaxed state, the child is exposed to the feared situation in small, gradual steps:

1. He is encouraged to relax (see Relaxation Training, p. 170).
2. Adult discusses the child's fear or anxiety.
3. She encourages him to define the fear in specific terms.
4. She lists specific aspects of his fear on separate pieces of paper.
5. Child is asked to rank the aspects of his fear in order, with the most fear-inducing first and the least fear-inducing last.
6. He is encouraged to remain in a relaxed state.
7. He is asked to raise his finger when he feels anxious.
8. Adult asks child to imagine the least fear-inducing aspect on the list.
9. If he indicates anxiety, she asks him to stop, encourages him to relax and suggests something pleasurable for him to imagine.
10. If he shows no anxiety, and after the item has been fully explored, the next most fear-inducing item is dealt with.
11. The process is repeated until the child is able to remain relaxed when exposed to the most fear-producing aspect.

Notes

- Deep relaxation is a crucial part of the process: the child must know how to become relaxed (see Relaxation Training, p. 170), and undergoes prior training in this.
- Exposure to fear-producing stimuli begins with a few seconds only, and is thereafter gauged according to the child's reaction.
- He may be exposed to actual objects, animals, insects, real-life situations and so on rather than being asked to imagine them.
- Sessions always end with a successful exposure—e.g., a return to an easier item on the list.
- Constant praise and encouragement are crucial if the child is to maintain his motivation for treatment.
- If he does not respond, his fears and anxieties may be rooted in deeper problems.

Time out

Aim

- To minimise the reinforcement of undesirable behaviour and the possibility of physical and emotional harm to the child or to others.

Method

The reinforcer—whatever it is that appears to be promoting the undesirable behaviour—is removed from the child, or the child is removed from the reinforcer.

1 Adult decides what is reinforcing his unacceptable behaviour.
2 She decides whether to remove him or the reinforcer.
3 She decides how long he and the reinforcer will remain apart.
4 She explains to him the reason why he is being separated from the reinforcer.
5 Child is separated from the reinforcer.
6 He and the reinforcer are reunited after the specified time.

Notes

- When the child is denied the reinforcer he should not be placed in a situation that he finds more pleasurable: accordingly, the time-out period should be preplanned.
- The time-out period should not be excessive.
- Time out should be administered and linked to the undesirable behaviour as soon as it appears.
- After time out, the child should be fully supported.

The token economy system

Aim

- To establish the required behaviour.

Method

1 Adult selects the behaviour to be achieved.
2 She decides on the token system (see Notes below).
3 Child is awarded tokens (and praise) when he meets requirements.

4 He accumulates tokens and later exchanges them for rewards.
5 Adult gradually phases out tokens, but maintains reinforcement with praise and so on.

Notes

THE TOKEN SYSTEM

- The required behaviour must be achievable by the child.
- The behaviour must be clearly defined and expressed to him.
- The observation of the token system must be restricted to a certain time and location.
- The system must be clearly defined to him. The explanation should include:
  —the time and location for its observation
  —the number of times a behaviour will be required before tokens are awarded
  —the number of tokens to be awarded
  —a description of the available rewards (and the number of tokens required to gain them)
  —an explanation of the conditions under which tokens may be withdrawn for undesirable behaviour.
- The available rewards should be meaningful to the child.
- While tokens *may* be withdrawn for unacceptable behaviour, this should be done very infrequently—the emphasis should be on rewarding acceptable behaviour.

IMPLEMENTATION

1 Display the system on a simple chart.
2 Praise the child when awarding a token.
3 Never be drawn into an argument about tokens to be awarded.
4 Record the tokens awarded.
5 Gradually extend the time and location for the observation of the system and the award of tokens.
6 Gradually phase out tokens, but maintain the focus on providing non-material rewards for desirable behaviour—e.g., praise, the awarding of responsibilities, the provision of shared pleasurable experiences.

THERAPIES

Counselling

Aim

- To encourage the child to share his problems, explore alternative solutions and arrive at a personal decision regarding the resolution of his difficulties.

Method

The adult and the child form a relationship that promotes his self-disclosure, his self-examination and the resolution of the problem.

1. Adult explains the way in which sharing his feelings about his problems may help.
2. As he describes these difficulties, she reflects them back to him and encourages him to explore the surrounding issues.
3. She encourages him to think about how his difficulties may be overcome.
4. She guides him towards his own action plan.
5. He is gradually encouraged to become less dependent on her.

Notes

- To create a trusting relationship in which the child feels able to share his problems, the adult emphasises her *unconditional acceptance* of him. Despite his problems, she accepts him—she focuses on being non-judgemental.
- To promote a feeling of self-worth in the child and the confidence to express his inner feelings, the adult is alert to and focuses on the positive aspects of his life.
- She attempts to empathise with him and to understand his thoughts and feelings.
- Her responses affirm that she understands what the child is saying: e.g., after he has expressed himself, she may repeat what he has said in a summary statement.
- She focuses on listening.
- Her responses to what the child has said are not over-prescriptive: she focuses on listening, then gently and gradually, and only if necessary, guides him towards a solution.

Psychoanalysis

Aim

- To discover, and purge the child of, any underlying reasons (stemming from unconscious conflicts) for his behaviour; to relate them to present difficulties and, with the insight gained, to help him make appropriate adjustments.

Method

1. The adult creates a warm, non-judgemental, trusting relationship with the child.
2. Using a variety of techniques such as free association—in which he is encouraged to say the first thing that comes to mind—and the relating of dreams, the adult encourages him to reveal his innermost thoughts and feelings.
3. She interprets the child's 'evidence'.
4. She helps him to appreciate the interpretation.
5. She helps him to relive, and come to terms with, significant unpleasant past experiences, either verbally or through such activities as play and drawing.
6. She helps him to adjust his behaviour.

Notes

- Revealing the past may be counterproductive and even harmful for some children.

Gestalt therapy

Aim

- To resolve and complete 'unfinished business'—internal conflicts—thereby enhancing the child's capacity to think and feel without distortion.

Method
The adult encourages the child to explore his present thoughts and feelings and, by the use of various techniques (see Notes below), to bring underlying issues to resolution.

1 She encourages him to express how he feels in the 'here and now'.
2 She encourages him to crystallise and explore these feelings.
3 She helps him to consider how his feelings may relate to 'unfinished business' from the past.
4 She helps him to complete 'unfinished business' (see Notes below).
5 She promotes in him self-reliance and responsibility for his own actions (see Notes).

Notes

- Child is encouraged to use 'I' rather than 'they', 'you' or 'it' so as to promote a sense of personal responsibility and control.
- He may be asked to sit facing an empty chair and speak to another, imaginary, person with problems as if that person were present, with the aim of encouraging him to express himself fully without inhibition.
- He may be asked to reverse roles and express himself as though he were the other, imaginary, person, as a means to appreciating that other person's perspective.
- He may be asked to behave in the opposite way to that in which he normally would, thereby appreciating the alternative benefits.
- He may be asked to describe a recent dream. Using a number of techniques, the adult encourages him to explore issues inherent in the dream, thereby bringing them to 'completion'.
- The adult is alert to non-verbal signals, such as foot-swinging, tone of voice and posture, which may signal unspoken stress points.

Rational emotive therapy

Aim

- To help the child become more rational in his beliefs and as a consequence to become less negative, intolerant and self-derogatory.

Method

The adult helps the child to realise that he may have underlying beliefs that are adversely affecting the way he behaves, and encourages him to think of alternative, more positive, ways of viewing situations and responding to them.

1 She examines:
 —the degree of negative interpretation used by the child
 —his intolerance
 —his self-denigration.
2 She examines the 'faulty' underlying—broad or specific—beliefs that may be at the root of the child's thinking.
3 She challenges his 'self-talk' (see Notes below).
4 She encourages him to consider the adverse effect of his beliefs and the benefit of taking an alternative rational approach.
5 She helps him—through demonstration, role-play and imagery—to develop a more rational approach and a more positive form of 'self-talk'.
6 She explores different ways of responding to the same situation or person.
7 She teaches him how to cope in the most commonly encountered situations.
8 He is taught to reward himself when he has coped successfully in a real-life situation.

Notes

- The formula for rational emotive therapy can be expressed as ABCDE, where A = activating events, B = faulty belief, C = consequent behaviour, D = disputing the faulty belief, E = better behavioural effects.
- The adult focuses on disputing the child's faulty beliefs.
- There are three common beliefs that are at the root of a negative view of life:
 —the child feels that he must do well if he is to avoid being cast aside as worthless
 —he feels that the world should be castigated for treating him so unkindly
 —he feels that life will be intolerable if his needs are not immediately met.

- 'Self-talk' refers to our inner speech, whereby we express our feelings to ourselves and are able to organise and plan our lives.
- The adult focuses on inculcating positive inner talk within the child.
- She varies the level of intensity of disputing according to the child's needs; with younger children she may elicit their faulty beliefs through play or drawing.

Interpersonal cognitive problem-solving

Aim

- To encourage the child to analyse situations, to appreciate the point of view of others and to think of alternative ways of behaving.

Method
The adult encourages the child to:

1 describe a specific problematic situation and how he feels about it
2 think of reasons for the situation, including the perspective of others and their and his feelings
3 think of the costs and benefits of taking alternative approaches
4 think of how he may arrive at a satisfactory solution.

Notes
The adult emphasises:

- the causal relationship between events
- the consequences of events
- the need to pinpoint the target to be achieved and to think how it may be reached
- an appreciation of the thoughts and feelings of others
- the need to consider a variety of alternative ways of behaving.

Stress-inoculation training

Aim

- To help the child cope with stress.

Method

The adult teaches the child to prepare for and deal with situations that cause him difficulty:

1. She encourages him to prepare for a situation by using positive 'self-talk' as a way of helping him to resist coming under stress.
2. She helps him to deal with a stressful situation by rehearsing appropriate behaviour.
3. She teaches him to be aware of when he is becoming stressed.
4. She teaches him simple coping techniques (e.g., deep breathing, counting to ten).

Notes

- Self-talk, as we noted earlier, is the child's inner speech that he can use to control his feelings and actions.
- In order to develop a conscious sense of self-control, the adult encourages the child to continually reflect—verbally, or in writing, drawing or role-play—on his management of stressful situations and people.

Self-instruction training

Aim

- To help the child solve problems.

Method

In encouraging the child to use self-talk, the adult promotes four skill areas:

1. the ability to identify a problem
   —'What exactly is happening?' 'What should I do?'
2. the ability to pay attention and respond appropriately
   —'Someone is speaking—listen carefully.' 'What courses of action have I now open to me?' 'Which one should I pursue?' 'What will be the outcome?'
3. the ability to self-evaluate and to reinforce good behaviour
   —'How am I doing now?' 'I'm pleased with my effort.' 'I feel good.'

4 the ability to correct himself and to cope
—'I shouldn't have done that.' 'This is what I'll do instead.'

Transactional analysis

Aim

- To help the child appreciate the nature of his present reactions to others and to interact in an alternative and more productive way.

Method
The adult encourages the child to appreciate the various sorts of transactions that take place between people, and how a positive outcome can result from adopting a different stance. She helps the child to appreciate:

1 how we may act, whatever our age
—as a child, who feels, wants, plays and manipulates
—as a parent, who controls, criticises, punishes, nurtures and protects
—as an adult, who has self-control and takes a reasonable, rational approach to solving problems.
2 how problems can arise when two people involved in an interaction play different roles
3 how we give or collect positive or negative 'strokes' (see Notes, below) to or from another person
4 how the child may alter his stance and his 'strokes' so as to resolve specific problematic situations.

Notes

- A 'stroke' is any action that promotes feelings in another person.
- Strokes can be negative (discouraging) or positive (encouraging).
- Adult and child draw up contracts in which target behaviours, and the means whereby they are to be achieved, are clearly expressed.

Psychosynthesis

Aim

- To promote a greater sense of self-control in the child and to minimise his sense of frustration.

Method
The adult helps the child to 'disidentify' from his feelings and to take a more realistic view of his circumstances.

1 She strengthens his sense of self by encouraging him to:
—examine his present circumstances in detail, with an emphasis on the positive aspects
—develop his willpower, through regular and demanding physical exercise.
2 She reduces his inner frustration by:
—encouraging him to examine his ideal model—his idea of what things should be like—and his personal heroes
—helping him to debunk them, to adopt a more realistic view of them.
3 When his sense of identity is strengthened and his self-esteem is high, she helps him to appreciate that:
—he remains constant and separate from his changing body, intellect and emotions
—he has 'subpersonalities'
—he can disidentify with these subpersonalities and remain in a position of control.

Notes

- To prevent the process from developing into an unfruitful game, the child is kept unaware of the ultimate goal.
- The 'strengthening' process must be fully completed if the disidentification stage is not to be abused by the child by his blaming his actions on subpersonalities.

Family therapy

Aim

- To consider and, where necessary, adjust interactions within the family in order to alleviate problems being experienced by the child.

Method

The therapist assesses the child's problems within the context of the family and agrees with family members on a course of action:

1. The family is examined in terms of:
   —its structure, the status of each member
   —how its members communicate, solve problems and express their feelings
   —specific problematic areas created by internal or external factors.
2. A set of targets is prioritised with family members, and appropriate contracts are formulated.
3. Members are helped to adjust their roles and interactions in order to achieve targets.
4. A support system is devised to cope with future relapses.

Notes

- The family may be seen as a 'system' which has many 'subsystems', such as a parent subsystem, a sibling subsystem and a spouse subsystem.
- The family system is considered in the context of greater systems—e.g., the neighbourhood or an ethnic or religious group.
- Within each system there are hierarchies and rules which govern the behaviour of its members.
- Some systems are 'closed' and do not change in the face of circumstances; others are 'open', and adjust to their environments.
- A child's problems—or those of other family members—although appearing to create disharmony may, because of their intensity, be a unifying, stabilising influence on the family system.

The treatment approaches outlined above may be used along with many others in a variety of combinations.

* * *

Drug treatment

Aim

- To alleviate a child's condition when environmental adjustments on their own are ineffective; to avoid the development of other, 'secondary', behavioural problems.

Method
After diagnosis of the child's condition, medication is prescribed, then adjusted as necessary.

1 The medication available includes antipsychotic medication, antidepressant medication; anti-anxiety medication; anticonvulsant medication; medication for sleep disorders, medication for enuresis, medication for attention deficits and hyperactivity.
2 The child may enter a hospital school for assessment and a trial medication period.
3 The medication is administered appropriately, and the child's behaviour and any side effects are carefully monitored.
4 Regular reassessment of the continued need for medication is undertaken.

Note

- Although there are indications that in certain instances medication on its own can be highly effective, it is usually considered as complementary to adjustments at home and at school.

CONCLUSION

Using a combination of these and many other techniques, a specialist will be able to supplement the work you are already doing with the difficult child, whether at home or at school. Whatever happens, you will become heavily involved in the treatment process.

As a parent, you may be encouraged to take part in family therapy, to implement a specific programme of behaviour modification, or to monitor the effect of your child's medication. You will undoubtedly be asked to provide a profile of your family and to discuss many of the issues we have covered earlier. As a teacher, you may be asked to make a number of adjustments to your classroom routine or to implement a particular strategy such as a token economy system (see p. 173). You may be asked to ensure that the child receives his medication, and to monitor the effect it has on his behaviour.

For any treatment to succeed it will be necessary for you and your child to take a positive attitude towards it. This may not be easy, for most treatment will take many weeks, months or even years to complete, and your child may lose interest. He will be relying on your sustained enthusiasm to keep him going. Inherent to success with all the techniques I've described is the assumption that the child is willing to take part, that he wants to be helped. Older children in particular find it very hard to accept that they need help. They are often unsure of themselves to begin with, and may interpret the slightest suggestion that they need help as severe criticism. So you will need to think carefully about how you are going to approach the issue.

If you feel that you are not likely to have much success, arrange for someone whom he trusts and respects to take him out and, when the moment is right, to tactfully broach the problem of his behaviour and what can be done about it. He will need to be gently guided towards making his own decision, rather than to be told what is to happen. If he is able to feel that he has done this the pleasure of being in control may prove to be the first step towards the resolution of his difficulties.

* * *

In this book we have considered a number of questions that parents and teachers regularly ask themselves when they are living or working with a difficult child. We have also looked at the nature of childhood disorders, and examined strategies that may help to minimise their impact. In doing so, I hope you have begun to feel more objective about the behaviour of your child and that you are now more able to look to the future with hope rather than despair.

Appendix A: **Useful Information**

UK RESOURCES

1 If you are in need of immediate support, use the telephone:

Mind*info*line
Granta House, 15–19 Broadway, Stratford, London E15 4BQ.
Tel: 0208 519 2122 (London), 0345 660 163 (outside London)

Parent Network
2 Winchester House, 11 Cranmer Road, London SW9 6EJ.
Tel: 0207 735 1214

Parentline
Endway House, The Endway, Hadleigh, Essex SS7 2AN.
Helpline: 01702 554782

The Samaritans
10 The Grove, Slough, Berkshire SL1 1QP.
Helpline: 0345 909090

2 There are many other organisations that work in the field of mental health: all of them will be able to offer you help and advice, or put you in touch with someone who can. Here are some of them:

INFORMATION SERVICES offering advice and information on a wide range of mental health problems:

Mental Health Foundation
20–21 Cornwall Terrace, London NW1 4QL.

Tel: 0207 535 7400 E-mail: mhf@mentalhealth.org.uk
Website: http://www.mentalhealth.org.uk

Young Minds
102–108 Clerkenwell Road, London ECIM 5SA.
Tel: 0345 626376

SUPPORT FOR FAMILIES

Contact a Family
170 Tottenham Court Road, London W1P 0HA.
Tel/Helpline: 0207 383 3555 Fax: 0207 383 0259
E-mail: info@cafamily.org.uk
Website: www.cafamily.org.uk

Home-Start UK (branches throughout the UK)
2 Salisbury Road, Leicester LE1 7QR.
Tel: 0116 233 9955 Fax: 0116 233 0232

Parent Network (see p. 186 for address)

ASSESSMENT

As I have repeatedly emphasised, only an expert will be able to make an effective diagnosis of your child's disorder. If you are at all concerned, consult your general practitioner and your child's teachers, who will recommend to you a specialist in your area. A number of independent consultants provide assessment services. Here is just one:

Learning and Assessment Centre
2nd Floor, 44 Springfield Road, Horsham, West Sussex
RH12 2PD. Tel: 01403 240002 Fax: 01403 260900
This is an independent (NHS and private) organisation specialising in the comprehensive multidisciplinary assessment of children and adolescents with concentration, hyperactivity, behavioural and learning problems.

3 Some organisations focus on particular problems:

Attention-Deficit Disorder Information Services
PO Box 340, Edgware, Middlesex HA8 9HL.
Tel: 0208 905 2013 Fax: 0208 386 6466
E-mail: Addis@compuserve.com

Manic *Depression* Fellowship
8–10 High Street, Kingston upon Thames, Surrey KT1 1EY.
Tel: 0208 974 6550

British *Dyslexia* Association
98 London Road, Reading, Berkshire
RG1 5AU. Helpline: 0118 9668271

Eating Disorders Association
1st Floor, Wensum House, 103 Prince of Wales Road,
Norwich, Norfolk NR1 1DW.
Tel: 01603 619090 Helpline: 01603 621414

Association of Workers for Children with *Emotional and Behavioural Difficulties*
Charlton Court, East Sutton, Maidstone, Kent ME17 3DG.
Tel: 01622 843104 Website: http://www.mistral.co.uk/awcebd

National *Schizophrenia* Fellowship
28 Castle Street, Kingston upon Thames, Surrey
KT 4NS. Tel: 0208 547 3937 Advice line: 0208 974 6814

4 If you want to find the right school for your child:

The following publications will provide you with details of all the schools in the UK:

Education Authorities Directory and Annual (current year)
The School Government Publishing Company, Darby House,
Bletchingly Road, Merstham, Redhill, Surrey RH1 3DN.

Special Schools in Britain (current year)
Network Publishing Ltd, Palmer House, Palmer Lane,
Coventry CV1 1FN.

Which School? for Special Needs (current year)
John Catt Educational Ltd, Great Glemham, Saxmundham, Suffolk IP17 2DH.

USA RESOURCES

A range of Mental Disorders (including Depression and Schizophrenia)
NAMI (National Alliance for the Mentally Ill)
Helpline: 1-800-950

The John Hopkins Hospital
600 N. Wolfe Street, Baltimore, MD 21287.
Tel: (410) 955-3863

Depression
National Depressive and Manic-Depressive Association
730 N. Franklin Street, Suite 501, Chicago, Il 60610-3526.
Tel: (800) 826-3632 Fax: (312) 642-7243

Eating Disorders
The Centre for Eating Disorders
St. Joseph's Medical Center, 7620 York Road, Towson, Maryland 21204-7582.
Tel: (410) 427-2100

Learning Disabilities
Learning Disabilities Association of America
4156 Library Road, Pittsburgh, Pennsylvania 15234.
Tel: (412) 341-1515 Fax: (412) 344-1224

Attention Deficit (Hyperactivity)
CHADD (Children with Attention Deficit Disorder)
499 Northwest 70th Avenue, Suite 308, Plantation, Florida 33317.

Dyslexia
Dyslexia-ADD Treatment Center
940 Saratoga Avenue, Suite 205, San José, CA 95129.
Tel: (408) 241-3330 Fax: (408) 241-2473
E-mail: response@dyslexia-add.com

Dyslexia Association of America
Central Offices, 532 E. Shiawasse Street, Lansing, MI 48912.
Tel: (517) 485-4000 Freephone: 1-800-832-3535
Fax: (517) 485-4076

Autism
Autism Society of America
7910 Woodmont Avenue, Suite 650, Bethesda,
MD 20814-3015.
Tel: (301) 657-0881 Fax: (301) 657-0869

Aspergers
ASPEN of America (Asperger Syndrome Educational Network of America, Inc.)
P.O. Box 2577, S. Jacksonville, FL. 32203-2577.
Helpline: (904) 745-6741

Anxiety/Obsessive-Compulsive/Tic Disorders
UCLA Neuropsychiatric Institute
760 Westwood Plaza, Room 68-251, Los Angeles,
CA 90024-1759.
Tel: (310) 825-0122

If you are on the Internet . . .

Some addresses are provided above. In addition, a huge amount of other information on a wide range of child and adolescent disorders is available. Try:

Child and Adolescent Psychiatry On-Line:
http://www.priory.com/psychild.htm

Mental Health Net Disorders and Treatments:
http://www.cmhc.com/dxtx.htm

You can share your concerns with other parents and professionals by logging on to the forum of your interest—they exist for most disorders.

* * *

Alan Train, the author of this book and of others relating to dealing with difficult children, provides a private consultancy for parents and is available for talks to parent support groups and professionals.
Tel: 01403 260772 E-mail: alan-train@talk21.com

Appendix B: **Diagnostic Criteria**

The following criteria are those presently recommended by the American Psychiatric Association. They are reprinted, with that organisation's permission, from the *Diagnostic and Statistical Manual of Mental Disorders*, 4th edition.

■ Diagnostic criteria for attention-deficit/hyperactivity disorder

A Either (1) or (2):

(1) six (or more) of the following symptoms of **inattention** have persisted for at least six months to a degree that is maladaptive and inconsistent with developmental level:

Inattention

(a) often fails to give close attention to details or makes careless mistakes in schoolwork, work or other activities

(b) often has difficulty sustaining attention in tasks or play activities

(c) often does not seem to listen when spoken to directly

(d) often does not follow through on instructions and fails to finish schoolwork, chores, or duties in the workplace (not due to oppositional behaviour or failure to understand instructions)

(e) often has difficulty organising tasks and activities

(f) often avoids, dislikes or is reluctant to engage in tasks that require sustained mental effort (such as schoolwork or homework)

(g) often loses things necessary for tasks or activities (e.g., toys, school assignments, pencils, books or tools)

(h) is often easily distracted by extraneous stimuli
(i) is often forgetful in daily activities

(2) six (or more) of the following symptoms of **hyperactivity-impulsivity** have persisted for at least six months to a degree that is maladaptive and inconsistent with developmental level:

Hyperactivity
(a) often fidgets with hands or feet or squirms in seat
(b) often leaves seat in classroom or in other situations in which remaining seated is expected
(c) often runs about or climbs excessively in situations in which it is inappropriate (in adolescents or adults, may be limited to subjective feelings of restlessness)
(d) often has difficulty playing or engaging in leisure activities quietly
(e) is often 'on the go' or often acts as if 'driven by a motor'
(f) often talks excessively

Impulsivity
(g) often blurts out answers before questions have been completed
(h) often has difficulty awaiting turn
(i) often interrupts or intrudes on others (e.g., butts into conversations or games)

B Some hyperactive-impulsive or inattentive symptoms that caused impairment were present before age seven years.

C Some impairment from the symptoms is present in two or more settings (e.g., at school or work and at home).

D There must be clear evidence of clinically significant impairment in social, academic or occupational functioning.

E The symptoms do not occur exclusively during the course of a pervasive developmental disorder, schizophrenia or other psychotic disorder and are not better accounted for by another mental disorder (e.g. mood disorder, anxiety disorder, dissociative disorder, or a personality disorder).

Code based on type:

F90.0 Attention-deficit/hyperactivity disorder, combined type: if both criteria A1 and A2 are met for the past six months

F98.8 Attention-deficit/hyperactivity disorder, predominantly inattentive type: if criterion A1 is met but criterion A2 is not met for the past six months

F90.0 Attention-deficit/hyperactivity disorder, predominantly hyperactive-impulsive type: if criterion A2 is met but criterion A1 is not met for the past six months

Coding note: For individuals (especially adolescents and adults) who currently have symptoms that no longer meet full criteria, 'in partial remission' should be specified.

■ Diagnostic criteria for F91.8 conduct disorder

A A repetitive and persistent pattern of behaviour in which the basic rights of others or major age-appropriate societal norms or rules are violated, as manifested by the presence of three (or more) of the following criteria in the past twelve months, with at least one criterion present in the past six months.

Aggression to people and animals

(1) often bullies, threatens, or intimidates others
(2) often initiates physical fights
(3) has used a weapon that can cause serious physical harm to others (e.g., a bat, brick, broken bottle, knife, gun)
(4) has been physically cruel to people
(5) has been physically cruel to animals
(6) has stolen while confronting a victim (e.g., mugging, purse-snatching, extortion, armed robbery)
(7) has forced someone into sexual activity

Destruction of property

(8) has deliberately engaged in fire-setting with the intention of causing serious damage
(9) has deliberately destroyed others' property (other than by fire-setting)

Deceitfulness or theft

(10) has broken into someone else's house, building or car

(11) often lies to obtain goods or favours or to avoid obligations (i.e., 'cons' others)
(12) has stolen items of non-trival value without confronting a victim and without breaking and entering (e.g., shoplifting, forgery)

Serious violations of rules
(13) often stays out at night despite parental prohibitions, beginning before age thirteen years
(14) has run away from home overnight at least twice while living in parental or parental surrogate home (or once without returning for a lengthy period)
(15) is often truant from school, beginning before age thirteen years

B The disturbance in behaviour causes clinically significant impairment in social, academic or occupational functioning.

C If the individual is age eighteen years or older, criteria are not met for antisocial personality disorder.

Specify type based on age at onset:
Childhood-onset type: onset of at least one criterion characteristic of conduct disorder prior to age ten years
Adolescent-onset type: absence of any criteria characteristic of conduct disorder prior to age ten years

Specify severity:
Mild: few if any conduct problems in excess of those required to make the diagnosis *and* conduct problems cause only minor harm to others
Moderate: number of conduct problems and effect on others intermediate between 'mild' and 'severe'
Severe: many conduct problems in excess of those required to make the diagnosis *or* conduct problems cause considerable harm to others

▪ Diagnostic criteria for F91.3 oppositional defiant disorder

A A pattern of negativistic, hostile and defiant behaviour lasting at least six months, during which four (or more) of the following are present:
(1) often loses temper
(2) often argues with adults

(3) often actively defies or refuses to comply with adults' requests or rules
(4) often deliberately annoys people
(5) often blames others for his or her mistakes or misbehaviour
(6) is often touchy or easily annoyed by others
(7) is often angry and resentful
(8) is often spiteful or vindictive

Note: Consider a criterion met only if the behaviour occurs more frequently than is typically observed in individuals of comparable age and developmental level.

B The disturbance in behaviour causes clinically significant impairment in social, academic or occupational functioning.

C The behaviours do not occur exclusively during the course of a psychotic or mood disorder.

D Criteria are not met for conduct disorder, and, if the individual is age eighteen years or older, criteria are not met for antisocial personality disorder.

■ Diagnostic criteria for F84.0 autistic disorder

A A total of six (or more) items from (1), (2) and (3), with at least two from (1), and one each from (2) and (3):

(1) qualitative impairment in social interaction, as manifested by at least two of the following:

(a) marked impairment in the use of multiple non-verbal behaviours such as eye-to-eye gaze, facial expression, body postures, and gestures to regulate social interaction
(b) failure to develop peer relationships appropriate to developmental level
(c) a lack of spontaneous seeking to share enjoyment, interests or achievements with other people (e.g., by a lack of showing, bringing, or pointing out objects of interest)
(d) lack of social or emotional reciprocity

(2) qualitative impairments in communication as manifested by at least one of the following:

(a) delay in, or total lack of, the development of spoken

language (not accompanied by an attempt to compensate through alternative modes of communication such as gesture or mime)

(b) in individuals with adequate speech, marked impairment in the ability to initiate or sustain a conversation with others

(c) stereotyped and repetitive use of language or idiosyncratic language

(d) lack of varied, spontaneous make-believe play or social imitative play appropriate to developmental level

(3) restricted repetitive and stereotyped patterns of behaviour, interests and activities, as manifested by at least one of the following:

(a) encompassing preoccupation with one or more stereotyped and restricted patterns of interest that is abnormal either in intensity or focus

(b) apparently inflexible adherence to specific, non-functional routines or rituals

(c) stereotyped and repetitive motor mannerisms (e.g., hand- or finger-flapping or -twisting, or complex whole-body movements)

(d) persistent preoccupation with parts of objects

B Delays or abnormal functioning in at least one of the following areas, with onset prior to age three years: (1) social interaction, (2) language as used in social communication, or (3) symbolic or imaginative play.

C The disturbance is not better accounted for by Rett's disorder or childhood disintegrative disorder.

■ Diagnostic criteria for F84.5 Asperger's disorder

A Qualitative impairment in social interaction, as manifested by at least two of the following:

(1) marked impairment in the use of multiple non-verbal behaviours such as eye-to-eye gaze, facial expression, body postures, and gestures to regulate social interaction.

(2) failure to develop peer relationships appropriate to developmental level

(3) a lack of spontaneous seeking to share enjoyment, inter-

ests or achievements with other people (e.g., by a lack of showing, bringing, or pointing out objects of interest to other people)

(4) lack of social or emotional reciprocity

B Restricted, repetitive and stereotyped patterns of behaviour, interests and activities, as manifested by at least one of the following:

(1) encompassing preoccupation with one or more stereotyped and restricted patterns of interest that is abnormal in either intensity or focus

(2) apparently inflexible adherence to specific, non-functional routines or rituals

(3) stereotyped and repetitive motor mannerisms (e.g., hand- or finger-flapping or -twisting, or complex whole-body movements)

(4) persistent preoccupation with parts of objects

C The disturbance causes clinically significant impairment in social, occupational and other important areas of functioning.

D There is no clinically significant general delay in language (e.g., single words used by age two years, communicative phrases used by age three years).

E There is no clinically significant delay in cognitive development or in the development of age-appropriate self-help skills, adaptive behaviour (other than in social interaction), and curiosity about the environment in childhood.

F Criteria are not met for another specific pervasive developmental disorder or schizophrenia.

■ Criteria for major depressive episode

A Five (or more) of the following symptoms have been present during the same two-week period and represent a change from previous functioning; at least one of the symptoms is either (1) depressed mood or (2) loss of interest or pleasure.

Note: Do not include symptoms that are clearly due to a general medical condition, or mood-incongruent delusions or hallucinations.

(1) depressed mood most of the day, nearly every day, as

indicated by either subjective report (e.g., feels sad or empty) or observation made by others (e.g., appears tearful). *Note:* In children and adolescents, can be irritable mood.

(2) markedly diminished interest or pleasure in all, or almost all, activities most of the day, nearly every day (as indicated by either subjective account or observation made by others)

(3) significant weight loss when not dieting or weight gain (e.g., a change of more than 5 per cent of body weight in a month), or decrease or increase in appetite nearly every day. *Note:* In children, consider failure to make expected weight gains.

(4) insomnia or hypersomnia nearly every day

(5) psychomotor agitation or retardation nearly every day (observable by others, not merely subjective feelings of restlessness or being slowed down)

(6) fatigue or loss of energy nearly every day

(7) feelings of worthlessness or excessive or inappropriate guilt (which may be delusional) nearly every day (not merely self-reproach or guilt about being sick)

(8) diminished ability to think or concentrate, or indecisiveness, nearly every day (either by subjective account or as observed by others)

(9) recurrent thoughts of death (not just fear of dying), recurrent suicidal ideation without a specific plan, or a suicide attempt or a specific plan for committing suicide

B The symptoms do not meet criteria for a mixed episode.

C The symptoms cause clinically significant distress or impairment in social, occupational or other important areas of functioning.

D The symptoms are not due to the direct physiological effects of a substance (e.g., a drug of abuse, a medication) or a general medical condition (e.g., hypothyroidism).

E The symptoms are not better accounted for by bereavement, i.e., after the loss of a loved one, the symptoms persist for longer than two months or are characterised by marked functional impairment, morbid preoccupation with worthlessness, suicidal ideation, psychotic symptoms or psychomotor retardation.

Diagnostic criteria for schizophrenia

A *Characteristic symptoms*: Two (or more) of the following, each present for a significant portion of time during a one-month period (or less if successfully treated):
  (1) delusions
  (2) hallucinations
  (3) disorganised speech (e.g., frequent derailment or incoherence)
  (4) grossly disorganised or catatonic behaviour
  (5) negative symptoms, i.e., affective flattening, alogia or avolition

Note: Only one criterion A symptom is required if delusions are bizarre or hallucinations consist of a voice keeping up a running commentary on the person's behaviour or thoughts, or two or more voices conversing with each other.

B *Social/occupational dysfunction:* For a significant portion of the time since the onset of the disturbance, one or more major areas of functioning such as work, interpersonal relations or self-care are markedly below the levels achieved prior to the onset (or when the onset is in childhood or adolescence, failure to achieve expected level of interpersonal, academic or occupational achievement).

C *Duration:* Continuous signs of the disturbance persist for at least six months. This six-month period must include at least one month of symptoms (or less if successfully treated) that meet criterion A (i.e, active-phase symptoms) and may include periods of prodromal or residual symptoms. During these prodromal or residual periods, the signs of the disturbance may be manifested by only negative symptoms or two or more symptoms listed in criterion A present in an attenuated form (e.g., odd beliefs, unusual perceptual experiences).

D *Schizoaffective and mood disorder exclusion:* Schizoaffective disorder and mood disorder with psychotic features have been ruled out because either (1) no major depressive, manic or mixed episodes have occurred concurrently with the active-phase symptoms; or (2) if mood episodes have occurred during active-phase symptoms, their total duration has been brief relative to the duration of the active and residual periods.

E *Substance/general medical condition exclusion*: The disturbance is not due to the direct physiological effects of a substance (e.g., a drug of abuse, a medication) or a general medical condition.

F *Relationship to a pervasive developmental disorder:* If there is a history of autistic disorder or another pervasive developmental disorder, the additional diagnosis of schizophrenia is made only if prominent delusions or hallucinations are also present for at least a month (or less if successfully treated).

Classification of longitudinal course:

Episodic with inter-episode residual symptoms (episodes are defined by the re-emergence of prominent psychotic symptoms); *also specify if:* **with prominent negative symptoms**

Episodic with no inter-episode residual symptoms

Continuous (prominent psychotic symptoms are present throughout the period of observation); *also specify if:* **with prominent negative symptoms**

Single episode in partial remission; *also specify if:* **with prominent negative symptoms**

Single episode in full remission

Other or unspecified pattern

Less than one year since onset of initial active-phase symptoms

Bibliography

American Psychiatric Association (1994). *Diagnostic and Statistical Manual of Mental Disorders*, 4th edition. American Psychiatric Association, Washington DC.

Angold, A. (1989). Structured assessment of psychopathology in children and adolescents, in Thompson, C. (ed.), *The Instruments of Psychiatric Research*. John Wiley, Chichester.

Angold, A, and Rutter, M. (1992). Effects of age and pubertal status on depression in a large clinical sample, *Development and Psychopathology*, 4: 5–28.

Attwood. T. (1998). *Asperger's Syndrome*. Jessica Kingsley, London.

Azar, S. T. and Siegel, B. R. (1990). Behavioural treatment of child abuse: a developmental perspective, *Behaviour Modification*, 14.

Barkley, R. A. (1997). *Defiant Children: A Clinician's Manual for Assessment and Parent Training*. Guilford Press, New York.

Bernard, M. E. and Joyce M. R. (1984). *Rational Emotive Therapy with Children and Adolescents*. Wiley, New York.

Berne, E. (1961). *Transactional Analysis in Psychotherapy*. Souvenir Press, London.

Bloomquist, M. L. (1996). *Skills Training for Children with Behaviour Disorders—a Parents' and Therapist's Guidebook*. Guilford Press, New York.

Bowlby, J. (1980). *Attachment and Loss: Sadness and Depression*, vol. 3. Basic Books, New York.

Brophy, J. E., and Good, T. L. (1974). *Teacher–Student Relationships: Causes and consequences*. Holt, Rinehart & Winston, New York.

Cantor, S. (1988). *Childhood Schizophrenia*. Guilford Press, New York.

Cantwell, D. P. (1988). DSM-III studies, in Rutter, M., Tuma,

A. H., and Lann, I. S. (eds), *Assessment and Diagnosis in Child Psychopathology*. David Fulton, London.

Cantwell, D. P., and Baker, L. (1991). Psychiatric classification, in Michels, R. et al. (eds), *Psychiatry*. Lippincott, Philadelphia.

Caron, C., and Rutter, M. (1991). Comorbidity in child psychopathology: concepts, issues and research strategies, *Journal of Child Psychology and Psychiatry*, 32: 1064–80.

Clausen, J. A., and Yarrow, M. R. (1955). Paths to the mental hospital, *Journal of Social Issues*, 11: 25–32.

Coopersmith, S. (1967). *The Antecedents of Self-Esteem*. Freeman, San Francisco.

Cottrell, D., Hill, P., Walk, D., Dearnaly, J. and Ierotheou, A. (1988). Factors influencing non-attendance at child psychiatry outpatient appointments, *British Journal of Psychiatry*, 152: 201–4.

Donnellan, A. M., LaVigna, G. W., Negri-Shoultz, N., and Fassbender, L. L. (1988). *Progress without Punishment—Effective Approaches for Learners with Behaviour Problems*. Columbia University Press, New York and London.

Dunn, J. (1988). Connections between relationships: implications of research on mothers and siblings, in Hinde, R., and Stevenson-Hinde, J. (eds), *Relationships within Families: Mutual Influences*. Oxford University Press, Oxford.

Earls, F. (1985). Oppositional-defiant and conduct disorders, in Rutter M., Taylor, E., and Hersov, L. (eds), *Child and Adolescent Psychiatry*, 3rd edition. Blackwell Scientific Publications, Oxford.

Ellis, A., and Bernard, M. E. (eds) (1983). *Rational-emotive Approaches to the Problems of Childhood*. Plenum, New York.

Faupel, A., Herrick, E., and Sharp, P. (1998). *Anger Management*. David Fulton, London.

Finkelhor, D., and Korbin, J. (1988). Child abuse as an international issue, *Child Abuse and Neglect*, 12.

Freud, A. (1946). *The Psychoanalytic Treatment of Children*. Imago, London.

Garalda, M. E., and Bailey, D. (1986). Children with psychiatric disorders in primary care, *Journal of Child Psychology and Psychiatry*, 27: 611–24.

Goldstein, S. (1997). ADHD and childhood depression: the hidden co-morbidity, in Markus, R. (ed.), *AD/HD '97: Papers from the Oxford Conference*. IPS, Hurstpierpoint.

Goodman, R. (1993). Brain abnormalities and psychological development, in Hay, D. F., and Angold, A. (eds), *Precursors, Causes and Psychopathology*. John Wiley, Chichester.

Graham, P., and Rutter, M. (1968). The reliability and validity of the psychiatric assessment of the child. II: interview with the parent, *British Journal of Psychiatry*, 114: 581–92.

Graziano, A. M. (ed.) (1971). *Behavior Therapy with Children*. Aldine, New York.

Harrington, R., Fudge, H., Rutter, M., Pickles, A., and Hill, J. (1991). Adult outcomes of childhood and adolescent depression. Links with antisocial disorder, *Journal of the American Academy of Child and Adolescent Psychiatry*, 30: 434–9.

Heath, A. C., and Martin, N. G. (1988). Teenage alcohol use in the Australian twin register: genetic and social determination of starting to drink, *Alcoholism: Clinical and Experimental Research* 12.

Herbert, M. (1978). *Conduct Disorders of Childhood and Adolescence*. John Wiley, Chichester.

Herbert, M. (1981). *Behavioural Treatment of Problem Children: A Practice Manual*. Academic Press, London.

Hersov, L. (1985). Faecal soiling, in Rutter, M., Taylor, E., and Hersov, L. (eds), *Child and Adolescent Psychiatry*, 3rd edition. Blackwell Scientific Publications, Oxford.

Hinde, R. (1988). Continuities and discontinuities: conceptual issues and methodological considerations, in Rutter, M. (ed.), *Studies of Psychosocial Risk: The Power of Longitudinal Data*. Cambridge University Press, Cambridge.

Hoghughi, M. (1988). *Treating Problem Children*. Sage Publications, London.

Jenkins, J. M., and Smith, M. A. (1990). Factors protecting children living in disharmonious homes: maternal reports, *Journal of the American Academy of Child and Adolescent Psychiatry*, 29: 60–9.

Johnson, B. D., Wish, E. D., Scheidler, J., and Huizinga, D. (1991). The concentration of delinquent offending: serious drug involvement and high delinquency rates. *Journal of Drug Issues*, 21.

Kewley, G. D. (1999). *Attention Deficit Hyperactivity Disorder: Recognition, Reality and Resolution*. LAC Press, Horsham.

Klein, R. G. (1985). Anxiety disorders, in Rutter, M., Taylor, E., and Hersov, L. (eds), *Child and Adolescent Psychiatry*, 3rd edition. Blackwell Scientific Publications, Oxford.

Lapouse, R., and Monk, M. (1958). An epidemiological study of behaviour characteristics in children, *American Journal of Public Health*, 48: 1134–44.

Leckman, J. F., and Cohen, J. F. (1985). Tic disorders, in Rutter, M., Taylor, E., and Hersov, L. (eds), *Child and Adolescent Psychiatry*, 3rd edition, Blackwell Scientific Publications, Oxford.

Madonna, P., van Scoyk, S., and Jones, D. P. H. (1991). Family interaction within incest and non-incest families, *American Journal of Psychiatry*, 148.

Meichenbaum, D. H. (1983). *Coping with Stress*. Century, London.

Mental Health Foundation (1999). *Annual Report 1997/98*. Mental Health Foundation, London.

Minuchin, S., and Fishman, H. C., (1981). *Family Therapy Techniques*. Harvard University Press, Cambridge, Mass.

Nelson-Jones, R. (1982). *The Theory and Practice of Counselling*. Holt, Rinehart & Winston, London.

Offord, D. R., and Fleming, J. E. (1991). Epidemiology, in Lewis, M. (ed.), *Child and Adolescent Psychiatry: A Comprehensive Textbook*. Williams & Wilkins, Baltimore.

O'Rourke, K., and Worzbyt, J. C. (1996). *Support Groups for Children*. Taylor & Francis, Washington D.C.

Parry-Jones, W. L. (1985). History of child and adolescent psychiatry, in Rutter M., Taylor, E., and Hersov, L. (eds), *Child and Adolescent Psychiatry*, 3rd edition. Blackwell Scientific Publications. Oxford.

Patterson, G. R. (1982). *Coercive Family Process*. Castilia, Eugene, Oregon.

Quinton, D., Rutter, M., and Gulliver, L. (1990). Continuities in psychiatric disorders from childhood to adulthood in the children of psychiatric patients, in Robins, R., and Rutter, M. (eds), *Straight and Devious Pathways from Childhood to Adulthood*. Cambridge University Press, New York.

Rapoport, J. L., and Ismond, D. R. (1996). *DSM-IV Training Guide for Diagnosis of Childhood Disorders*. Bruner/Mazel Inc., New York.

Ripley, K. (1999). Dyspraxia, in Lyons, R. (ed). *Lecture Notes for Developmental Disorders*. IPS, Hurstpierpoint.

Robin, A. L., and Foster, S. L. (1989). *Negotiating Parent–adolescent Conflict*. Guilford Press, New York.

Robins, L. N. (1991). Conduct disorder, *Journal of Child Psychology and Psychiatry* 32: 193–212.

Rogers, C. R. (1961). *On Becoming a Person*. Houghton Mifflin, Boston, Mass.

Ruskin, M., Rhode, M., Dubinsky, A., and Dubinsky, H. (eds) (1997). *Psychotic States in Children*. Duckworth, London.

Rutter, M. (1975). *Helping Troubled Children*. Penguin, Harmondsworth.

Rutter, M., Cox, A., Taplin, C., Berger, M., and Yule, W. (1975). Attainment and adjustment in two geographical areas. 1: The prevalence of psychiatric disorder, *British Journal of Psychiatry*, 126: 493–509.

Rutter, M., and Gould, M. (1985). Classification, in Rutter, M., and Hersov, L. (eds)., *Child and Adolescent Psychiatry: Modern Approaches*, 2nd edition, 304–431. Blackwell Scientific Publications, Oxford.

Sameroff, A. J., and Feil, L. A. (1983). Parental concepts of development, in Sigel, I. E. (ed), *Parental Belief Systems: The Psychological Consequences for Children*. Lawrence Erlbaum, New Jersey.

Sameroff, A. J., and Seifer, R. (1990). Early contributors to developmental risk, in Rolf, J., Masten, A. S., Cichetti, D., Neuchterlein, K. H., and Weintraub, S. (eds), *Risk and Protective Factors in the Development of Psychopathology*. Cambridge University Press, Cambridge.

Shaffer D. (1985). Enuresis, in Rutter, M., Taylor, E., and Hersov, L. (eds), *Child and Adolescent Psychiatry*, 3rd edition. Blackwell Scientific Publications, Oxford.

Shepherd, M., Oppenheim, B., and Mitchell, S. (1971). *Childhood Behaviour and Mental Health*. University of London Press, London.

Sherman, A. R. (1973). *Behaviour Modification: Theory and Practice*. Brooks/Cole, California.

Singleton, C. (1999). Dyslexia: latest research and its implications for classroom practice, in Lyons, R. (ed.), *Lecture Notes for Developmental Disorders*. IPS, Hurstpierpoint.

Skuse, D. (1985). Feeding and sleeping disorders, in Rutter, M., Taylor, E., and Hersov, L. (eds), *Child and Adolescent Psychiatry*, 3rd edition. Blackwell Scientific Publications, Oxford.

Spivack, G., and Shure, M. B. (1976). *The Problem-solving Approach to Adjustment*. Josey Bass, San Francisco.

Sroufe, L. A., Fox, N., and Pancake, V. (1983). Attachment and dependency in developmental perspective, *Child Development*, 55.

Steinhausen, H. C. (1985). Anorexia and bulimia nervosa, in Rutter, M., Taylor, E., and Hersov, L. (eds), *Child and Adolescent Psychiatry*, 3rd edition. Blackwell Scientific Publications, Oxford.

Stern, G., Cotterell, D., and Holmes, S. (1990). Patterns of attendance of child-psychiatry outpatients with special reference to Asian families, *British Journal of Psychiatry*, 156: 384–7.

Thomas, A., Chess, S., Birch, H. G. Hertzig, M. E., and Korn, S. (1963). *Behavioural Individuality in Early Childhood*. New York University Press, New York.

Thomas, A., Chess, S., and Birch, H. G. (1968). *Temperament and Behaviour Disorders in Children*. University of London Press, London.

Thomas, A., and Chess, S. (1982). Temperament and follow-up to adulthood, in Porter, R., and Collins, G.M. (eds), *Temperamental Differences in Infants and Young Children*. Pitman, London.

Train, A. (1996). *ADHD: How to Deal with Very Difficult Children*. Souvenir Press, London.

Treacher, A., and Carpenter, J. (eds) (1984). *Using Family Therapy*. Blackwell, Oxford.

Walens, S., DiGiuseppe, R., and Wessler, P. (1980). *Practitioner's Guide to Rational Emotive Therapy*. Oxford University Press, New York.

Webster-Stratton, C., and Herbert, M. (1996). *Troubled Families—Problem Children*. John Wiley, Chichester.

Weissman, M. M., Prusoff, B. A., Gammon, G. D., Merikangas, K. R., Leckman, J. F., and Kidd, K. K. (1984). Psychopathology in children (ages 6–18) of depressed and normal parents, *Journal of American Academy of Child Psychiatry*, 23: 78–84.

Werner, E. E., and Smith, R. S. (1992). *Overcoming the Odds: High-risk Children from Birth to Adulthood*. Cornell University Press, Ithaca, New York.

Werry, J. S., and Taylor, E. (1985). Schizophrenia and allied disorders, in Rutter, M., Taylor, E., and Hersov, L. (eds), *Child and Adolescent Psychiatry*, 3rd edition. Blackwell Scientific Publications, Oxford.

Werry, J. S., McClellan, J. M., and Chard, L. (1991). Childhood and adolescent schizophrenic, bipolar, and schizoaffective disorders: a clinical and outcome study, *Journal of the American Academy of Child and Adolescent Psychiatry*, 30: 457–65.

Wilkes, T. R., Belsher, G., Rush, A. J., Frank, E., and Associates (1994). *Cognitive Therapy for Depressed Adolescents*, Guilford Press, New York.

Wolfe, D. A. (1985). Child-abusive parents: an empirical review and analysis, *Psychological Bulletin*, 97.

Wolfe, D. A. (1987). *Child Abuse: Implications for Child Development and Psychopathology*. Sage, London.

Wolff, S. (1991). *Children Under Stress*. Penguin Books, London.

Wolff, S. (1995). *Loners*. Routledge, London and New York.

Index